ENVIRONMENTAL POLICY ANALYSIS

For my parents.

Environmental Policy Analysis

A General Equilibrium Approach

JIAN XIE

Ashgate

Aldershot • Brookfield USA • Singapore • Sydney

Published by
Ashgate Publishing Limited
Gower House
Croft Road
Aldershot
Hants GU11 3HR
England

Ashgate Publishing Company
Old Post Road
Brookfield
Vermont 05036
USA

Reprint 1998

British Library Cataloguing in Publication Data
Xie, Jian
   Environmental policy analysis : a general equilibrium
   approach
   1.Environmental policy 2.Environmental impact analysis
   3.Pollution 4.Environmental policy - China 5.Environmental
   impact analysis - China 6.Pollution - China
   I.Title
   333.7'14

Library of Congress Cataloging-In-Publication Data
Library of Congress Catalog Card Number: 96-85251

ISBN 1 85972 421 3

Printed and Bound by Biddles Limited
Guildford and King's Lynn

Contents

Part Two: An application to China

Tables

Figures

Preface

Environmental pollution is now a serious problem in many developing countries. One approach to combat the problem is to implement various pollution control policies. However, due to a lack of adequate quantitative models, the economic impacts and effectiveness of many pollution control policies are still unknown.

This book introduces a quantitative economic modeling framework for environmental policy analysis in developing countries. The book is divided into two parts. Part One uses the computable general equilibrium (CGE) approach to develop an integrated economic and environmental model for environmental policy analysis. The integrated model incorporates various environmental components, including pollution taxes, subsidies, and cleaning activities, into a standard CGE framework. Part one also presents an environmentally extended social accounting matrix (ESAM) that serves as a consistent data set for model calibration. The results of the research contribute theoretically to both the methodology of CGE modeling for environmental policy analysis and to environmental accounting.

Part Two applies the environmental CGE model to China, the largest developing country in the world, to evaluate the effectiveness of Chinese environmental policies on pollution control and their impacts on the Chinese economy. The environmental policies under scrutiny include pollution emission taxes, pollution abatement subsidies, household waste disposal taxes, and government spending on pollution cleaning services. The economic impacts of the wastewater treatment plan in China's recently launched five-year environmental protection program are also examined. A comparison of the simulation results of different policy alternatives is presented.

Acknowledgements

This research was conducted over two years between 1993 and 1995 at Cornell University. I am indebted to many people and organizations for their help during my work on this research. I would first like to thank professor Sidney Saltzman, my advisor at Cornell University. It was Sid Saltzman who strongly encouraged me when I explored this research topic. I owe so much to professors Walter Isard, Erik Thorbecke, and Iwan Azis. Professor Isard's seminar was very helpful in developing my analytical skills. Professor Thorbecke's course in development economics provided a great platform on which to develop my model. Professor Azis gave many suggestions and comments about my work in CGE modeling. I also would like to express my appreciation to professors Barclay Jones, Porus Olpadwala, and Levent Orman for all they did for me during my study at Cornell. Moreover, without financial support from the East Asia Program, the Mario Einaudi Center for International Studies, and the Program for International Studies in Planning at Cornell, my trips to China in the summers of 1993 and 1994 for data collection would have been very difficult.

Many people outside Cornell have helped, in one way or another, in my research. I am grateful to Keith Florig, Raymond Kopp, and Walter Spofford at Resources for the Future; Shantayanan Devarajan, Jeffrey Lewis, John O'Connor, and Zhi Wang at the World Bank; Richard Garbaccio at the East-West Center; Theodore Panayotou at the Harvard Institute for International Development; Christian Dufournaud at Waterloo University; and Dianqing Xu at the University of Western Ontario for their interest in my research and helpful discussions on this topic. Finally, I would like to thank many people in China who helped me during my field trips there. It is impossible to list them all here, I hope that someday I can express my thanks to them directly.

Abbreviations

CGE   Computable general equilibrium
ECGE   Environmental computable general equilibrium model
ESAM   Environmentally extended social accounting matrix
GDP   Gross domestic product
NEPA   National Environmental Protection Agency of China
RMB   Ren-Min-Bi, the name of Chinese money.
SAM   Social accounting matrix
SSB   State Statistical Bureau of China
Y   Yuan, the basic unit of the Chinese money. The official exchange rate in 1990 was that one yuan equaled 0.21 U.S. dollar.

Note: Abbreviations and variable names in the CGE model are listed in Table 5.3 in chapter 5 as well as in the GAMS program listing of the environmental CGE model in the appendix of the book.

1 Introduction

1.1 Environmental problems and the need for environmental policy modeling

Environmental problems are serious and pervasive in today's world. In many developing countries, industrial pollution emissions continue to increase and, as a result, environmental problems such as deforestation, soil erosion, and the expansion of desert areas are aggravated. These problems have severely threatened the sustainable development of these countries and have caused great concern at all levels, from the general public to national governments and international agencies.

Because their countries face serious environmental degradation, the governments of many developing countries have begun to introduce environmental policies and regulations to combat environmental problems. The most popular environmental policies include pollution taxes, environmental impact assessments, pollution subsidies, and pollution emission permits. However, due to a lack of adequate quantitative models for environmental policy analysis, the effectiveness of pollution controls and the economic impacts of these policies are still unknown. Therefore, there is a strong need for analytical models for environmental policy analysis.

The environmental problems of China, the largest developing country in the world, are serious and very important to the global environment. According to the 1993 Environmental Communiqué of China (NEPA, 1994), China, in that year, discharged 35.6 billion tons of wastewater, emitted 11.0 trillion cubic meters of waste gases (not including emissions from rural industry), and produced 620 million tons of solid waste. Air pollution was serious in large- and medium-size cities and had worsen in small cities. Moreover, acid rain occurred in many cities in southern China, and 69 per cent of surveyed urban river sections were polluted. The soil erosion area

1

expanded to 150 million hectares, 15.6 per cent of the total land; one-third of agricultural land was faced with significant soil erosion problems; and 6.67 million hectares of agricultural land was exposed to industrial wastes and urban refuse. China's environmental deterioration and its potential contribution to regional and worldwide environmental problems, such as global warming, large-scale acid rain, and the depletion of the ozone layer, have attracted worldwide attention.

In order to curb China's environmental problems, the government is implementing a series of environmental policies and programs. The major environmental policies and regulations include an environmental impact assessment system, an industrial pollution effluent fee system, environmental standards, and a pollution emission permit system. Recently, the government launched a five-year environmental protection program, through which the government hopes to treat 80 per cent of all industrial wastewater and 88 per cent of all industrial waste gases by 1998.

However, the economic impacts and effectiveness of these pollution control policies were largely unknown before the policies were implemented, mainly because of the lack of studies on environmental policy modeling. In order to design more effective environmental policies and assess the impacts of the policies on China's economy and environment, it is essential to develop quantitative models for Chinese environmental policy analysis. This need provided the application motivation for the research presented here.

1.2   Objectives and methodology

The primary objective of this book is to present an integrated economic and environmental model for environmental policy analysis, a model based on the computable general equilibrium (CGE) approach. This model incorporates various environmental components, such as pollution taxes, subsidies, and cleaning activities, into a standard CGE framework. In order to have a consistent equilibrium data set for calibrating the model, the book also presents an environmentally extended social accounting matrix (ESAM) framework. The results of the research contribute to the methodology of CGE modeling for environmental policy analysis and environmental accounting.

The secondary objective is to apply this model to China in order to analyze its environmental policies. This application and analysis are the first research of this type to be done for China. The environmental policies

2

under scrutiny in the case study include pollution emission taxes, pollution abatement subsidies, household waste disposal taxes, and government spending on pollution cleaning services. The economic impacts of the wastewater treatment plan in the recently launched five-year environmental protection program are also examined.

The CGE approach is adopted for environmental policy modeling in this research. Since the late 1980s, the CGE approach has been applied to environmental issues. Even though many of these applications still are in experimental stages, they show that the CGE approach has advantages for environmental policy modeling. Compared with other modeling techniques such as the input-output approach and linear programming, a CGE model has four appealing features for modeling for environmental policy analysis in the real world. First, prices are endogenous to the model and are determined by the 'market.' Second, the model focuses on an economy where supply and demand for either goods or production factors are equated by adjusting prices based on Walrasian general equilibrium theory. Third, supply and demand functions in the model are derived from the behavior of profit-maximizing producers and utility-maximizing consumers. Finally, the model is non-linear and contains resource constraints.

1.3   Outline

This seven-chapter book consists of two major parts: the theoretical model and a case study. Following this introductory chapter, chapter 2 reviews the literature in the fields of CGE modeling in general and environmental CGE models in particular. Chapter 3 develops an environmental CGE model. It begins with an introduction to the interactions between production and pollution, and then shows how to derive supply and consumption functions when pollution control costs are considered in a stylized 2-sector CGE model framework. The theoretical framework of a multi-sector environmental CGE model is developed in the last section of this chapter. Chapter 4 introduces the approaches taken in parameter specification of a CGE model. It first compares two parameter estimation approaches: the econometric approach and the calibration approach. Then it introduces the framework of an environmentally extended social accounting matrix (ESAM). The ESAM serves as a consistent equilibrium data set for parameter calibration of the environmental CGE model.

The case study of Chinese environmental policy analysis is presented in chapters 5 and 6. Using 1990 Chinese data, chapter 5 outlines the environmental CGE model for China and constructs an ESAM. The parameters of China's environmental CGE model are derived by calibrating the model to the 1990 ESAM of China. Several Chinese environmental policies and programs are simulated in chapter 6, and the major findings from those policy simulations are discussed. Chapter 7 contains a summary of the book, conclusions, and suggestions for further research. The appendix at the end of the book presents the GAMS program listing of the environmental CGE model for China.

Part One
AN ENVIRONMENTAL CGE MODEL

2 Literature review

This chapter reviews the literature in the fields of CGE modeling theory in general and environmental CGE models in particular. Section 2.1 introduces the basic concepts of CGE modeling and discusses the importance and advantages of CGE models in policy analyses. The recent progress in developing environmental CGE models is examined in the second section. Possible improvements to environmental CGE models are also discussed.

2.1   Computable general equilibrium modeling

Definition

Computable general equilibrium modeling, also known as applied general equilibrium (AGE) modeling, is concerned with converting the Walrasian general-equilibrium structure from an abstract representation of an economy into a realistic model of an actual economy (Shoven and Whalley, 1984). Although there is no precise definition of a CGE model, it can be described generally as a model that numerically specifies an economy 'where prices and quantities for goods and factors adjust to equate supply and demand based on Walrasian general equilibrium theory' (Condon et al., 1986). In particular, Bergman (1985) generalized three basic features of CGE models. First, supply and demand functions explicitly reflect the behavior of profit-maximizing producers and utility-maximizing consumers. Second, both quantities and relative prices are endogenous to the models, and the resource allocation patterns determined by the models have a strong flavor of Walrasian general equilibrium. Third, the models focus on the real side of the economy and situations in which the economy's resources are fully utilized.[1]

7

Why the CGE approach?

For several decades, input-output (I/O) type models, including I/O models and social accounting matrix (SAM) models, have been widely used in building multi-sector, economy-wide models for development planning and policy analysis.[2] Models of this type assume an economy that is linear in costs with exogenous demands and fixed prices, and result in partial equilibrium analysis. These models might be appropriate for short-run policy analysis, but their assumptions do not appear fitted to most real-world economies, ranging from capitalist to mixed economic systems,[3] like those of former East Bloc countries and China. In such economies, a great deal of the economic activity is not under the direct control of governments. In addition, price adjustments, nonlinear substitution possibilities, and supply and demand interactions, as well as limited resources, play important roles in their economic performance. To capture those real-world features, more general, nonlinear modeling techniques are required.

Unlike I/O type models, CGE models are characterized by nonlinear and price-endogenous features and the inclusion of resource constraints. They show great potential in capturing real-world problems. Devarajan (1988) specifically listed three reasons why CGE models, rather than other types of economy-wide models, are preferred for policy analysis. The first reason is that price matters. CGE models are distinguished by their price-endogenous feature. Prices and quantities are determined simultaneously in simulating the results of an external shock or a policy change. The second reason is that interactions matter. CGE models are designed to reflect many markets (such as goods and factor markets), many institutions (such as firms, households, and governments), and their interactions. The third reason is that economic structure matters. CGE models focus on the issue of economic structure.[4] In addition to its grasp of market mechanisms, the CGE approach leaves room for non-market activities. It has been shown that the CGE modeling technique has great flexibility for incorporating imperfectly competitive behavior, quantity or price adjustment lags, and widespread government intervention.[5]

With these advantages, the CGE approach is more capable of simulating the results of a policy change or an external shock than are other types of previous models, such as I/O models. CGE modeling emerged in 1960 (Johansen, 1960), and since the 1980s it has become a leading tool in multi-sector, economy-wide modeling for policy analysis.

8

The theoretical structure of CGE models has its roots in Walras's study of general equilibrium systems, dating back to the late nineteenth century. According to Scarf and Shoven (1984), Walras provided an elaborate mathematical description of a general equilibrium system for his time. However, Walras failed to provide an argument demonstrating the existence of an equilibrium solution. Based on the work of Arrow, Debreu, and others in the late 1940s and 1950s, the formulation of general equilibrium models was formalized to high degree of precision and generality; and the existence problem for the solution of the general equilibrium model was also solved. But the mathematical techniques available at that time offered no proof that the equilibrium quantities and prices of a general equilibrium system might be computed at all.[6] A computer algorithm for the numerical determination of the equilibrium of a Walrasian system was introduced by Scarf in 1967. Scarf's work (1967) finally led to an efficient numerical method of solving general equilibrium problems.

It is commonly agreed that applied CGE models started with Leif Johansen's model in 1960. In his doctoral dissertation 'A Multisectoral Study of Economic Growth,' Johansen presented a multi-sector, economy-wide model called the multi-sector growth model (MSG).[7] Johansen's MSG model is the first empirical implementation of general equilibrium models. While retaining Leontief's I/O system to describe inter-industrial relations, Johansen made the prices and quantities simultaneously determined in his model, in opposition to the input-output or linear programming techniques in which equilibrium quantities are determined at given prices and/or final demands.

Although Johansen's MSG model was incomplete in many aspects from today's point of view,[8] it inspired the present development of CGE models. The applications of CGE models began to boom in the 1970s.[9,10] Several surveys show that CGE models have been used for many countries, ranging from developed to developing countries, on various topics such as tax policy, international trade, income distribution, energy, natural resources, and the environment. For example, Shoven and Whalley (1984) examined two dozen CGE models of developed countries on taxes and trade. Devarajan et al. (1986), Decalume and Martens (1987), and Bandara (1991) listed about one hundred CGE models of developing countries. Today, CGE models have mushroomed everywhere. A complete survey in the entire field of CGE models is almost impossible. Surveys have to be focused on particular subsets of the models. Several examples of such surveys are de Melo's (1988) survey on trade policy, Bergman's (1988) on energy policy, and Devarajan's (1988) on natural resources.

Within the CGE framework are a variety of types of CGE models and a number of ways to classify them. Based on the underlying economic theories, Robinson (1991) divided CGE models of developing countries into two categories: neoclassical and structuralist. Neoclassical CGE models, pioneered by Dervis, de Melo, and Robinson (1982), are based on neoclassical theory. This group of models originally started at the World Bank and focused on the issues of structural adjustment in the medium term. Neoclassical CGE models assume profit-maximizing behavior by producers, utility maximization by consumers, and markets that clear through flexible adjustments in wages and prices. Structuralist CGE models, in contrast, have their roots in the political economy theories of Marx, Kalecki, Kaldor, and Keynes. These models focus on structural characteristics of the economy and are built on economic analyses of institutions and political economy.[11]

Bergman (1990a) grouped CGE models by four basic approaches, in chronological order. The first group originates with Johansen's MSG model. The second group, largely inspired by Harberger, Scarf, Shoven, and Whalley, is represented by a number of CGE models aimed at elucidating the efficiency and income distribution effects of trade or tax and transfer policies. The third group is the econometric approach of CGE modeling that is essentially based on the work of Jorgenson. The fourth group, based on the work of Ginsburgh and Waelbroeck, is characterized as an extension of activity analysis and linear programming modeling.

Besides Robinson's and Bergman's classifications, CGE models can also be divided into static, quasi-dynamic, and dynamic models, single-country and multi-country models, or calibration approach and econometric approach models.

Limitations of CGE models

As with other modeling techniques, the CGE approach has weaknesses and limitations.[12] First, most of the CGE models are deterministic in character, allowing no uncertainty in their model framework. Second, CGE modeling is very data-intensive. To reduce the demand for data, most CGE models are calibrated on a benchmark data set at a single year, which makes the models very sensitive to one-year data. Third, most CGE models are static or quasi-dynamic, with weak treatment of inter-temporal behavior such as investment behavior. Finally, many CGE models lack a representation of

10

money and financial sectors, and are thus unsuitable for fiscal policy analysis.

CGE modeling has also been criticized for its assumptions and practical limitations. The CGE approach has been attacked for its alleged reliance on market competition and constant-return-to-scale production functions. It has been argued both, that the quantity and price relationships in the model are too complicated and complex for decision makers and the general public to understand, and contrarily that the results of a CGE model tell nothing more than intuitive prediction would. A number of critics are also very skeptical about the reliability of the simulation results of CGE models, because their correctness cannot be tested.

Bandara (1991) and Devarajan, Lewis, and Robinson (1994) have discussed some of these criticisms. They indicate that CGE modeling has been able to overcome many of its alleged weaknesses. Meanwhile, in the last few years, several advances in CGE modeling have been made to overcome some of the limitations. First, the financial sector has been incorporated into the CGE framework (Bourguignon et al., 1989, Thorbecke, 1992, and Fargeix and Sadoulet, 1994), and thereby moving the CGE approach from conventional neoclassical CGE models toward macro models. Second, investment behavior has been more elaborately treated and the econometric approach more widely adopted in the parameter estimation of behavioral equations.[13] Third, efforts have been made to develop dynamic CGE models.[14] Finally, more efficient and user-friendly computer packages are being designed for users to more easily build CGE models.[15]

2.2   Environmental CGE models

Recently, there have been an increasing number of papers utilizing the CGE approach to assess the impacts of environmental policies on an economy and its environment. The reason for the growing interest in the CGE approach in environmental policy modeling is obvious. An environmental policy aimed at significantly reducing pollution emissions may have great effects on prices, quantities, and the structure of the economy. Thus, an analysis of the effects of such an environmental policy can only be conducted using a general equilibrium framework, instead of a partial equilibrium one (Conrad and Schroder, 1993).

Studies on incorporating environmental components into a CGE framework emerged in the late 1980s. Forsund and Strom (1988), Dufournaud, Harrington, and Rogers (1988), Bergman (1989), Hazilla and Kopp (1990),

Robinson (1990), and Jorgenson and Wilcoxen (1990) contributed to the early development of environmental CGE models. So far, about twenty stylized or applied environmental CGE models have been described in the literature. These models, in one way or another, endogenize pollution effects into production or utility functions. The models have been applied mainly to environmental and economic impact assessments of two groups of policies: public policies, such as taxation and government spending, and international trade policies.

A few of the first environmental CGE models have roots in Leontief's input-output model. Leontief (1970) presented a stylized environmental I/O table that incorporates a pollution cleaning sector and a physical account of pollutants in a conventional two-sector I/O table.[16] Based on the specification of the Leontief I/O table, Dufournaud, Harrington, and Rogers (1988), and Robinson (1990) built their environmental CGE models.

The economic part of Dufournaud, Harrington, and Rogers's model is standard in CGE modeling; constant elasticity of substitution (CES) sectoral production functions and a Cobb-Douglas utility function are used. To capture environmental effects in a CGE framework, they further included pollution outputs, with fixed pollution coefficients, and a pollution removal activity. They assumed that there was no private demand for the pollution cleaning activity, and that all pollutants would be removed by the government through its purchasing of the cleaning sector's output. The second assumption indicates that no pollutants would be discharged. In the model, the government purchase of the pollution cleaning service is financed either by a lump-sum income tax or an indirect tax on polluting sectors. The model is used to compare the effects of two different ways of financing the cleaning activity.

Robinson's model (1990) is also a general equilibrium adaptation of Leontief's stylized environmental I/O model. Like Dufournaud, Harrington, and Rogers, Robinson calibrated his model on Leontief's stylized data and assumed no private demand but only government demand for pollution cleaning. However, Robinson's model differs from that of Dufournaud, Harrington, and Rogers in its specification of sectoral production technology and in the assumed consumer behavior. The production side of Robinson's model is simplified by using Cobb-Douglas production functions with only two primary factors: labor and capital. To represent the societal effects of pollution emission and abatement activities, Robinson introduced a Stone-Geary utility function, in which pollution and cleaning activities are included. Robinson relaxed the rigid assumption of a zero-level of pollution emission in Dufournaud, Harrington, and Rogers's

12

model. He used fixed pollution coefficients in terms of sectoral outputs to estimate the amount of pollution generated, and presented pollution emissions into households' utility functions as public goods. Pollution cleaning is undertaken by the government and financed via Pigouvian taxes. Given a set of exogenously determined levels of pollution cleaning and tax rates, Robinson pointed out that the model solutions satisfy market equilibrium conditions but are not welfare-maximizing solutions. In order to generate fully optimal solutions, Robinson further constructed a nonlinear programming model. The CGE model equations serve as the constraints in the program, and pollution taxes and a government cleaning activity are included as policy instruments. The programming model simultaneously determines the optimum levels of these instruments, as well as the resulting market equilibrium. Using stylized data, Robinson showed the feasibility of including pollution within an optimizing framework in an economy-wide model.

Bergman (1990) presented an applied CGE model for impact assessment of reductions in air pollution emissions in Sweden. Bergman's model is a static, seven-sector, open-economy model. The technology of production is represented by a nested CES-Leontief production function in each production sector. There are four types of domestic inter-sectorally mobile factors of production in the model economy: capital, labor, electricity, and roundwood. The model includes pollution emissions and emission control activities, as well as markets and market prices for tradable emission permits. Pollution emissions from combustion and from industrial processes are distinguished in the model. There is also a distinction between old and new production units in some of the production sectors. The pollution abatement activity for each pollutant is modeled as a central abatement unit that sells cleaning services to the different sectors. The price of a cleaning service is equal to the marginal cost of abatement. The environmental policy goals are expressed as upper limits on total emissions. The government is assumed to sell emission permits, corresponding to maximum allowable total emissions, to the emitters of pollution at market prices. The cost of purchasing emission permits is incorporated into cost functions. A market for emission trading is assumed. The benchmark data of the model come from Sweden's 1985 I/O table. The results of Bergman's model suggest that major emission reductions are likely to have general equilibrium effects and, thus, that emission control cost functions that fail to take these effects into account may give a distorted picture of the economic impact of emission control.

In his latest work, Bergman (1993) further took into account the effects of environmental quality in utility maximization and productivity. He designed an environmental quality index and put the index into both utility and production functions.

Two other early CGE models for environmental policy analysis are worth mentioning in this literature review. One is Hazilla and Kopp's (1990) model; the other is Jorgenson and Wilcoxen's (1990) model. Both models are econometric general equilibrium models, following the pioneering work of Hudson and Jorgenson (1975).[17] An advantage of using the econometric approach in modeling producer behavior is that it allows for substitution possibilities among intermediate goods, which are ruled out in the calibration approach, and inter-temporal household consumption behavior. Besides, these two models have other features in common: (1) both are inter-temporal, multi-sector models; (2) both focus on the economic impacts of environmental regulations or programs; and (3) both consider only environmental costs, without taking environmental benefits into account.

Following the Hudson-Jorgenson framework, Hazilla and Kopp (1990) introduced their 36-sector, 1-consumer econometric CGE model of the U.S. economy to measure the social costs of environmental regulatory programs, such as the Clean Air and Clean Water acts. They believed that measuring social costs requires the use of a household's willingness to pay, rather than the compliance expenditure. They, therefore, modeled household preference using a hierarchy of indirect utility functions. Social welfare is measured using the expenditure function and the Hicksian notion of compensating variation. The expenditure function is derived from an econometrically estimated indirect utility function. The production of each sector, except for government services, is formulated as a hierarchical system of translog cost functions and econometrically estimated using U.S. data from 1958-1974. To estimate the social costs of environmental regulations, Hazilla and Kopp ran two simulations: one with the environmental programs and another without the programs. Their results show that social cost estimates diverge sharply from private cost estimates and that general equilibrium impacts, which cannot be reflected by using a static partial equilibrium analysis approach, such as the conventional cost-benefit analysis, are significant and pervasive.

Similarly, Jorgenson and Wilcoxen (1990) presented a 35-sector, 1-consumer econometric CGE model to analyze the economic impacts of U.S. environmental regulation. They estimated the costs of pollution control by simulating the long-term growth of the U.S. economy with and without environmental regulations. The model is a revised version of Jorgenson and

14

Slesnick's (1985) model. The production and consumption functions are econometrically estimated using time series-data from 1947-1985. The production function of each sector includes four factors: capital, labor, energy, and materials. Three types of pollution-related costs are represented in the translog price function for each polluting sector. They are pollution abatement costs, costs of investment for pollution control equipment, and costs of emissions controls on motor vehicles. By running the model with and without the pollution control costs, Jorgenson and Wilcoxen showed that pollution abatement has become a major claimant on the resources of the U.S. economy.

In addition to these public policy environmental CGE models, a small literature is emerging of works that use multi-country CGE models to look at international trade and global environmental questions. The models of Whalley and Wigle (1991), and Piggott, Whalley, and Wigle (1992) are early representatives of this group. Based on the early model of Whalley and Wigle (1990), Piggott, Whalley, and Wigle (1992) developed a static, multi-country CGE model of global trade and carbon emissions to analyze the international effects of carbon taxes. In their model, the world is divided into six regions. Each region is endowed with four non-traded primary factors of production: primary factors other than energy resources; carbon-based energy resources; other energy resources; and sector-specific skills and equipment in the energy-intensive manufacturing sector. Nested constant elasticity of substitution (CES) functions are used to represent production and demand in each region. One unique feature of the model is that the environmental benefits obtained from slowed global warming through reduced carbon emissions are incorporated into the utility function of each region. Piggott, Whalley, and Wigle examined a number of effects that either reinforce or weaken an individual country's incentive to participate. Using the model, they suggested the likely need for trade or other third-country sanctions, or incentive payments to support global agreements on carbon limitation.

More recently, there have been a rapid growth of CGE applications in the area of environmental policy analysis.[18] These CGE models are distinct from each other in how they integrate environmental components with economic activities. Environmental CGE models can be divided into several types, according to the level of pollution-related activities integrated into them. The first type of model is not very different from a standard CGE model.[19] It actually is an extended application of the standard CGE model. Extensions to standard CGE models include either estimating pollution emissions using fixed pollution coefficients per unit of sectoral outputs or intermediate inputs,[20] or exogenously changing prices or taxes concerning environmental regulations without any changes in model structure.[21] Extending the application of a standard CGE model in such ways does not affect the behavioral specifications of the standard CGE model, but does provide a more detailed description of production results from the environmental perspective.

The second type of environmental CGE model begins to introduce environmental feedback into economic systems. The models of this group, represented by Jorgenson and Wilcoxen's (1990) model, specify pollution control costs in production functions. A further extension of production specifications is to consider the effects of environmental quality on productivity. Examples of this type can be found in the models of Bergman (1993) and Gruver and Zeager (1994), which have environmental quality indices and incorporate those indices into production functions to capture the effects of pollution emissions on productivity.

To represent the effects of pollution emissions and abatement activities on consumption, a number of models incorporate environmental effects in utility functions. Robinson (1990) included net pollution emissions in a Stone-Geary utility function. Ballard and Medema (1993) also added the health damage to the Stone-Geary composite of consumption goods. Bergman (1993) specified the effects of environmental quality in a household utility function using an environmental quality index. Piggott, Whalley, and Wigle (1992) put the environmental benefits of carbon emission reduction into the utility function of their model.

Besides these modifications to production and consumption functions, a few models specify the production functions of pollution abatement activities or technologies. Robinson (1990) used a Cobb-Douglas production function to represent a pollution cleaning activity. Nestor and Pasurka (1994) modeled air pollution abatement processes and abatement tax rates based on an augmented input-output table that includes the inputs and outputs of air pollution abatement activities. Robinson, Subramanian, and Geoghegan (1993) identified polluting production processes and abatement technologies for each process. They assumed that a firm would use a particular abatement technology only if its marginal cost of abatement did not exceed the pollution emission charge.

Other recent attempts to improve environmental CGE modeling are presented briefly. By monetizing the impacts of air pollution on public health, Espinosa and Smith (1994) introduced the non-market environmental values in the specification of consumer preference. They also took a step in distinguishing the differential environmental impacts of production

16

activities at different locations in a multi-country CGE model. Noticing the importance of the lack of property rights in the environmental degradation of many developing countries, Devarajan (1993) suggested possible ways of incorporating the misuse of property rights into environmental CGE models for developing countries. Persson (1994) formulated the situation of undefined and well-defined property rights in a CGE model of deforestation in Costa Rica.

Although diverse CGE models have been applied to environmental policy analysis, environmental CGE modeling is still in its early stages, mainly for two reasons. The first is a relatively incomplete and unsophisticated specification of models of economic and environmental interactions. In many models, environmental externalities are weakly defined under rigid assumptions, or exogenously determined, which undermines the effectiveness and comprehensiveness of an environmental CGE model. The second reason is the lack of a well-defined environmental data framework that could provide a solid basis for numerical specification of an environmental CGE model. In addition, most of the existing environmental CGE models are still stylized and ad hoc in nature. Although a few models are applied to environmental issues in the real world, those models have mostly been built for developed countries. Few models have aimed at the environmental issues of developing countries.

In summary, this chapter reviewed the literature in the fields of CGE modeling theory in general and environmental CGE models in particular. It began with an introduction to the basic concepts of CGE modeling and the importance and advantages of CGE models in policy analyses. Recent progress in environmental CGE modeling was examined in the second section. Generally speaking, the chapter presented the need for and possible breakthrough points in building an environmental CGE model.

Notes

1   A few CGE models with financial sectors have been developed recently. These models are briefly described later in this section.

2   Applications of I/O models for policy analysis have been covered by various authors; see, for example, Miller and Blair (1985).

3   See Dervis, de Melo, and Robinson (1982) for more discussion. Comparing the multiplier matrices computed from the SAM accounts and by Jacobian differentiation of CGE models, Robinson

and Rolland-Holst (1988) further showed that the non-negative multiplier matrix from a SAM account is contradicted in an economy with resource limitations and flexible prices and, therefore, fails to consider the general equilibrium effects in the evaluation of economic policy in the real world.

4   By structure, Devarajan means 'proportions like the share of exports in GDP or the share of wages in value added.'

5   See, among others, Dervis, de Melo, and Robinson (1982) for a general description of CGE models. Burniaux and Waelbroeck (1992) presented a CGE model under imperfect competition for assessing the impacts of the 1992 integration program of the European Community on the world economy.

6   For example, when he introduced his multi-sector growth (MSG) model in 1960, Johansen got around the solution problem by linearizing his model and then solving it using simple matrix inversion.

7   See Johansen (1974, second, enlarged edition).

8   See Bergman (1985, pp.128) for a detailed discussion.

9   An explanation for the slow acceptance of CGE models is given by Bergman (1985).

10   Besides the merits of CGE modeling itself, several external reasons may play roles in the recent rapid growth of CGE models. They are: dissatisfactory performance of traditional planning models in handling the external shocks in the 1970s; the need for adequate tools to simulate the results of exogenous policy changes, such as taxes and subsidies; progress in the development of the underlying accounting framework; and development of efficient numerical solutions and computer software.

11   See Taylor (1990) for detailed descriptions of structuralist CGE models.

12   A number of authors have examined the weaknesses and criticisms of CGE modeling; see, for example, Arrow (1972), Scarf and Shoven (1984), Decaluwe and Martens (1987), and Bandara (1991).

13   See, for example, Jorgenson and Wilcoxen (1990), Hazilla and Kopp (1990), and Azis (1994).

14   See Adelman, Roland-Holst, and Sarris (1990) and Devarajan and Go (1993).

15   See, for example, Rutherford (1994).

16   Quite a number of scholars have contributed to environmental I/O models. Among others are Daly (1968), Isard (1969), Ayres (1969), and Victor (1972).

17   The econometric and calibration approaches in CGE modeling are discussed in detail in chapter 4.

18   A rough list of the recent papers on CGE modeling for environmental issues includes: Boyd and Uri (1991), Glomsrod, Vennemo, and Johnson (1992), Conrad and Schroder (1993), Ballard and Medema (1993), Blitzer et al. (1993), Lee and Roland-Holst (1993), Robins, Subramanian, and Geoghegan (1993), Lewis (1993), Azis (1993), Beghin, Rolland-Holst, and van der Mensbrugghe (1994), Copeland and Taylor (1994), Persson (1994), Dowlatabadi, Goulder, and Kopp (1994), Nestor and Pasurka (1994), Yeldan and Roe (1994), Gruver and Zeager (1994), Espinosa and Smith (1994), and McKibbin and Wilcoxen (1995).

19   The word 'standard' is somewhat vague. However, it is used in literature. A standard CGE model generally means the types of CGE model developed by the World Bank for developing countries to study structural change and international trade.

20   The models of Blitzer et al. (1993), Lee and Roland-Holst (1993), and Beghin, Rolland-Holst, and van der Mensbrugghe (1994) belong to this group.

21   See, for example, Boyd and Uri (1991).

3 Integrating environmental activities into the general equilibrium framework: an environmental CGE model

A conventional CGE model does not enable us to conduct environmental policy simulations. The only way to allow for such simulations is to have relevant environmental components built into the model. This chapter presents the technical specification of an environmental CGE model. The model aims at simulating the effects of environmental policies and environmental protection programs, such as pollution taxes and environmental standards, in developing countries.

Section 3.1 briefly introduces several basic concepts in environmental economics, such as environment-economy interactions, production externalities, and economic instruments for environmental protection. In order to illustrate the approach of modeling environment-economy interactions in a CGE framework, section 3.2 uses a stylized two-sector CGE model to discuss the behavioral changes of producers and consumers in response to pollution control policies and activities. A multi-sector environmental CGE model is presented in section 3.3 through a detailed description of each equation block of the model.

3.1 Environment-economy interactions

The economy and environment interact with each other in complex ways. To produce goods for consumption, a production process needs the environment to provide material resources and energy. The material resources and energy provided by the environment are transformed in the production and consumption processes, and the byproducts are then discharged back into the environment. The environment behaves as not only a provider of material resources and energy but also as the recipient of wastes generated from production and consumption. The environment's capacities to provide resources for and absorb wastes from an economy are limited. These limited capacities constrain the growth of the economy. Figure 3.1 is a simple diagram of environment-economy interactions.[1]

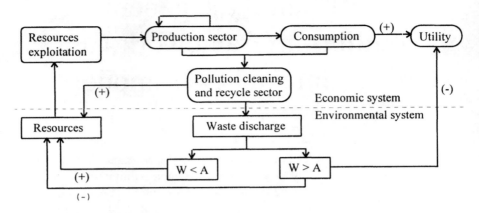

Figure 3.1 Environment-economy interactions

The diagram shows that an economic system not only takes resources from the environment but also discharges wastes into it. When the amount of wastes discharged into the environment (W) is larger than the environment's assimilative capacity (A), environmental degradation occurs. The degradation of environmental quality has direct negative effects on both the utility of consumers and the stock of resources. The decrease in the quantity and quality of resources also has an indirect impact on utility by reducing productivity.

Knowing the importance of the environment in an economy does not mean that polluters will voluntarily take responsibility for the negative impacts of their economic activities on the environment. This is because of the externalities of pollution damage caused by production and consumption activities. Production and consumption activities are usually conducted at the individual unit level, and their benefits exclusively go to each individual. Pollution emissions from production and consumption processes, however, cause loss to others. The environmental costs are external to polluters. Polluters, therefore, do not have incentives to account for these costs unless laws or regulations force them to do so.

To reduce pollution emissions, effective environmental protection instruments need to be chosen and implemented. Well-known economic instruments for pollution control include pollution taxes, pollution abatement subsidies, environmental standards, and marketable pollution permits.[2]

Many economists advocate tax pollution emissions. The tax rates can be based on the external costs of pollution emissions so that these costs can be internalized. Different from the pollution tax approach, the pollution abatement subsidy approach encourages polluters to install abatement equipment by providing a subsidy on the reduced amount of pollution. The environmental standards approach imposes environmental standards on pollution emissions and penalizes polluters that violate the standards. In the pollution permit system, the regulating authority allows only a certain level of pollution emissions, and issues emission permits up to the level. These pollution permits are tradable on a permit market.

The effectiveness of these pollution control instruments depends not only on their magnitudes but also on various other factors, such as prices, property rights, pollution damage, and pollution abatement technologies and costs. The major purpose of this study is to build a CGE model to analyze the impacts of alternative environmental policies on an economy and pollution control.

3.2 Producers' and consumers' reactions to pollution control: a stylized CGE model

As mentioned earlier, the classical CGE approach assumes that producers maximize profits and consumers maximize utility. Consumers' and producers' optimal behaviors are affected, in one way or another, by the effects of pollution emissions on production and consumption and the implementation of pollution control policies. Using of a stylized two-sector CGE model, this section discusses how compliance with environmental regulations changes the behavior of producers and consumers, and demonstrates a way of integrating environmental considerations into a CGE framework.

The original stylized two-sector CGE model without environmental considerations was introduced by Dinwiddy and Teal (1988). The model deals with a market-oriented economy of only two sectors (two kinds of products) and one household (consumer). To simplify matters, the model assumes that production sectors need only two primary inputs: capital and labor.

On the production side of the CGE model, each producer determines the optimal output level by minimizing the costs of the inputs and maximizing the profits of the outputs. If there are no pollution effects, the commodity supply functions can be derived simply from a two-stage optimization

23

procedure. First, suppose the production function for firm i takes the general form $X_i = X_i(K_i, L_i)$, where i=1 and 2; X_i is the output of firm (or sector) i; and K_i and L_i are capital and labor inputs, respectively. The least-cost combination of the factors under a given X_i is found from the solution to the cost-minimization problem:

Minimize $TC_i = r K_i + w L_i$
Subject to $X_{io} = X_{io}(K_i, L_i)$

where TC_i represents the total costs of firm i; X_{io} is the desired level of output; and r and w are prices for capital and labor. Next, the firm's short-run supply function (X_i) is determined by a total profit (π_i) maximization problem:

Maximize $\pi_i = P_i X_i - r K_i - w L_i$

where P_i is the price of product i.

When pollution occurs in production processes and certain pollution control activities, such as pollution abatement or pollution emissions taxation, are required, the profit maximization problem described above needs to be changed. The producer needs to adjust the output level based on new costs and new production functions containing pollution effects. Figure 3.2 illustrates the impacts of pollution on production.

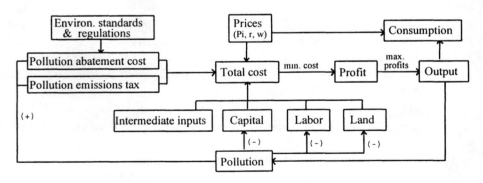

Figure 3.2 Pollution-production interactions

First, Figure 3.2 shows that the producer's total cost includes not only the costs of factor inputs but also pollution-related costs due to environmental protection requirements. Two types of pollution control costs are specified. One is pollution emission taxes and the other is the

24

costs of removing pollution in order to comply with environmental standards. No changes in production technology to meet pollution control requirements are assumed. Second, Figure 3.2 shows that pollution, in many cases, affects productivity directly. Pollution emissions degrade environmental quality, which then affects the quality and quantity of production factors: fixed capital, labor, and land. The degradation of fixed capital and labor causes productivity to decrease.

Assume that two types of pollutants (g=1 or 2) are generated from a production sector i. Given the impacts of pollution on production, the producer's profit maximization problem can be modified in the following two ways. First, the producer's total cost in the profit-maximization problem needs to include pollution and abatement costs. The cost function is, therefore, altered as:

$$TC_i = r\,K_i + w\,L_i + (\textstyle\sum_g T^e{}_g e_{gi}(1-\alpha_g))X_i + (\textstyle\sum_g P^a{}_g e_{gi}\alpha_g)X_i$$

where e_{gi} is the amount of pollutant g generated by producing a unit of output X_i; $T^e{}_g$ is the pollution emission tax levied on a unit of pollutant g emitted; $P^a{}_g$ is the price of pollution abatement service g; and α_g is the cleanup rate of pollution g. The term $(\sum_g T^e{}_g\, e_{gi}(1-\alpha_g))$ represents the pollution emission cost per unit output of sector i; and the term $(\sum_g P^a{}_g\, e_{gi}\,\alpha_g)$ is the pollution abatement cost per unit output of sector i. In the model, $P^a{}_g$ is endogenously determined by the interaction between supply and demand for pollution cleanup g; and $T^e{}_g$ is exogenously set by the government.

Second, the effect of environmental degradation on productivity can be reflected by defining K and L as functions of the total pollution emission or of an environmental quality index.

How about the consumption side of the model? Without pollution effects, household demands for two goods, C_1 and C_2, in the CGE model can be derived from a utility maximization problem of a representative household. The household maximizes its utility subject to the budget constraint that the household's total expenditures for the two goods must equal the household's income (Y). This can be written in the following mathematical form:

Maximize $U=U(C_1, C_2)$
Subject to $P_1C_1 + P_2C_2 = Y$

Solving the optimization problem provides the demand functions for C_1 and C_2.

However, when pollution occurs, it will influence the household's decisions about consumption. The interactions among pollution, pollution control, and consumption are shown in Figure 3.3.

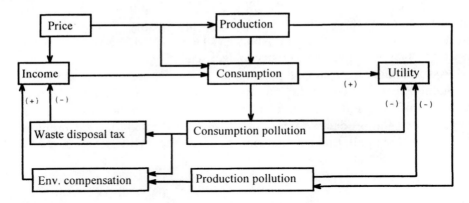

Figure 3.3 Pollution-consumption interactions

Figure 3.3 shows two ways that pollution can affect the consumption side of an economy: a decrease in utility and a change in household disposable income. The household suffers from environmental degradation caused by consumption and production pollution emissions. Therefore, the more pollution the household 'consumes,' the less utility it has.

Two possible effects of pollution control activities on household disposable income are also identified in Figure 3.3. The first effect is the payments the household makes to dispose of its waste. Payments for trash taxes and motor vehicle waste gas emission taxes are two examples. The second effect is a nominal increase in household income through polluters' compensation for environmental damage to the household. For example, a farmer may get compensation from a factory that discharges wastewater onto the farmer's land.

To capture the influence of pollution on consumption, the utility-maximizing problem of household consumption needs to be altered in the following three ways. First, the utility function needs to reflect the pollution effects. To model the negative impacts of pollution emissions on utility, the utility function needs to include environmental quality or pollution emissions. Second, the household expenditure for waste disposal should be subtracted from the household's income. Third, the compensation for environmental damage to the household, if any, should be added to the household income.

26

The new optimization problem for consumption demands, therefore, is:

Maximize $\quad$ $U=U(C_i, E_g, i,g=1,2)$

Subject to $\quad$ $\Sigma_i P_i C_i = Y + \Sigma_g a_g T^e_g E_g - \Sigma_g T^w_g \Sigma_i w_{gi} C_i$

E_g, $g=1$ and 2, represents the amount of pollutant g emitted from both firms and 'consumed' by the household. The parameter a_g is a distributional ratio, representing the share of pollution emission taxes used to compensate for damage to the household caused by pollution g. Its value is exogenously determined within [0, 1]. The term $a_g T^e_g$, thus, represents the compensation to the household for the environmental damage caused by the emissions of a unit of pollutant g. The remains of the pollution emission taxes (i.e., $(1-a_g)T^e_g$) are used for cleaning up other types of damage to the environment. Finally, w_{gi} is the pollution coefficient of consumption for pollutant g and good i, and T^w_g is the waste disposal tax rate on type g of consumption waste.

To eliminate pollution (as a means of satisfying pollution emission requirements), pollution abatement is required in many economies. Figure 3.4 depicts a representative pollution abatement sector.

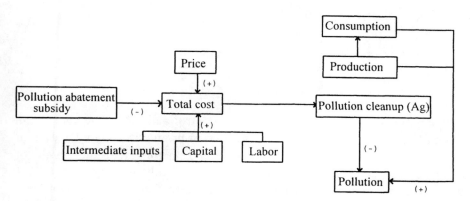

Figure 3.4 A pollution abatement sector

Unlike that of a production sector, the output of a pollution abatement sector (A_g) is the value of the pollution cleanup. Pollution cleanup can be viewed as special goods that are purchased at a certain price (P^a_g) by polluters in order to reduce their pollution emission levels. The optimal output level of a pollution abatement sector can be determined in the same way as that of a production sector. The price of a pollution abatement service is assumed to be determined implicitly by the market. Such an assumption is likely true in a situation where pollution is treated in profit-seeking waste treatment plants, such as in a privately-owned wastewater treatment plant. However, this assumption is unrealistic when pollution abatement facilities or sectors are affiliated with an individual factory, because built-in pollution abatement sectors or facilities are not likely to pursue a maximum profit strategy on their own. In this case, P^a_g can be fixed at the level of the average cost of pollution abatement.

To complete the stylized CGE model, equilibrium equations are needed for clearing the product markets: $C_1 = X_1$ and $C_2 = X_2$, and for clearing the factor markets:

$$K_1 + K_2 + \sum_g K_g = K^*, \text{ and}$$
$$L_1 + L_2 + \sum_g L_g = L^*$$

where K^* and L^* denote the exogenously fixed total quantities of capital and labor supplies; and K_g and L_g are the capital and labor demands of pollution abatement sector g.

Consumer's income (Y) is defined as:

$$Y = w L^* + r K^* + \pi_1 + \pi_2$$

The level of pollution emission is given in the equation:

$$E_g = \sum_i e_{gi} X_i - A_g$$

By solving the model with pollution control activities, one can obtain the equilibrium solutions of the composition of production, the allocation of production factors, the prices of goods and factors, and the levels of pollution emissions and pollution abatement simultaneously. Table 3.1 summarizes the equations of the original stylized CGE model and its two possible environmental extensions, one including the pollution emission tax only and the other further adding pollution abatement sectors. Numerical experiments for the three types of models have been conducted using the numerical specifications of Dinwiddy and Teal (1988). The results from these models show that the environmental CGE models are very useful in analyzing the environment-economy interactions and assessing the impacts of changes in various economic and environmental variable values on an economy and the environment.

Table 3.1
Conceptual framework of three stylized CGE models

<u>Model A</u> (the original model without environmental components)

Demand side

	Maximize	$U=U(C_1, C_2)$	(1)
	Subject to	$P_1C_1+P_2C_2=Y$	(2)

Supply side (for each firm or sector)

	Minimize	$TC_i=rK_i+wL_i$	(3)
	Subject to	$X_{io}=X_{io}(K_i, L_i)$	(4)
then	Maximize	$\pi_i=P_iX_i-TC_i$	(5)

Market clearing

$$C_1=X_1 \text{ and } \quad C_2=X_2 \qquad (6\text{-}7)$$
$$K_1+K_2=K^* \quad \text{and} \quad L_1+L_2=L^* \qquad (8\text{-}9)$$

Income

$$Y=wK^*+rL^*+\pi_1+\pi_2 \qquad (10)$$

<u>Model B</u> (add pollution emission tax to Model A)

Replace (1) with   Max $U=U(C_1, C_2, E_1, E_2)$

Replace (2) with $P_1C_1+P_2C_2=Y+P^e_1E_1+P^e_2E_2$

Replace (3) with $TC_i=rK_i+wL_i+(\sum_m P^e_m e_{mi})X_i$
$$i=1, 2. \qquad (11)$$

and define $E_m=\sum_i e_{mi}X_i$, m=1,2.

<u>Model C</u> (add pollution abatement sectors to Model B)

Replace (11) with

$$TC_i=rK_i+wL_i+(\sum_m P^e_m e_{mi}(1-\alpha_m))X_i+(\sum_m P^a_m e_{mi}\alpha_m)X_i$$

Define $E_m=\sum_i e_{mi}X_i-A_m$

$\alpha_m=A_m/\sum_i e_{mi}X_i$

where A_m is the amount of pollutant m treated.

Add pollution abatement sector m, m=1, 2.

	Production function	$A_m=A_m(K_m, L_m)$
	Minimize	$TC_m=rK_m+wL_m$
	and then maximize	$\pi_m=P^a_m A_m-rK_m-wL_m$

Notes:

(1) K^*, L^*, and P^e_m for m=1, 2, are exogenous.

(2)   Income Y is equal to factor payment minus income tax only.

3.3   A multi-sector environmental CGE model

After discussing the representation of the environment-economy interactions in a stylized CGE model, this section presents the technical specification of the multi-sector environmental CGE model developed by the author. The economic part of the model is similar to that of other applications of CGE models to developing countries.[3] Specifically, it is an adapted version of the Cameroon models developed by Condon, Dahl, and Devarajan (1986) and Devarajan, Lewis, and Robinson (1991).[4] However, the model presented here is unique in the way it integrates various pollution control activities with economic activities in a CGE framework. The environmental part of this model includes mainly: (1) pollution abatement activities and pollution abatement costs (or payments) of production sectors; (2) pollution taxes, such as production pollution emission taxes and household waste disposal taxes; (3) pollution control subsidies; (4) environmental compensation; and (5) various pollution indicators, including pollution cleanup ratios and the levels of pollution abatement and emissions. The model can be characterized as an integrated economic and environmental model in the line of the CGE approach.

The model assumes an economy having n production sectors and a representative household group. There are m types of pollutants generated from production and consumption processes and m pollution abatement sectors, each of which treats only one type of pollution. Production and pollution abatement sectors need intermediate inputs and two primary factors: capital and labor. The government and trade with the rest of the world are included in the model. The model is static with the capital demand of each sector exogenously determined.

Following closely the notation convention used in Devarajan, Lewis, and Robinson's model, the model presented here adopts (a) uppercase letters for endogenous variables, (b) Greek letters or lowercase letters for parameters, and (c) uppercase letters with a bar or lowercase letters for exogenous or control variables. The indices for sets used in the model are: ip and jp = 1, 2, ... n, representing production sectors; g and ia = 1,2,...m, representing pollutants and pollution abatement sectors; and i and j = 1,2,..., n, n+1, ..., n+m, containing both production and pollution abatement sectors. They appear as lowercase subscripts.

The model has over fifty equations or equation groups. They are divided into eight equation blocks. A complete list of variables and parameters with units can be found in Table 5-3 of chapter 5, where the

30

model is applied to China. A description of the equations by blocks is provided below.

(1) Price block There are a total of ten different groups of average prices in the model. They are composite good prices (P), domestic good prices (PD), capital input prices (PK), domestic prices of imports and exports (PM and PE), prices of intermediate inputs (PN), value-added prices (PVA), world prices of imports and exports (PWM and PWE), and output prices (PX). The relationships among these prices are sketched in Figure 3.5, and the equations defining prices in the model are presented in Table 3.2.

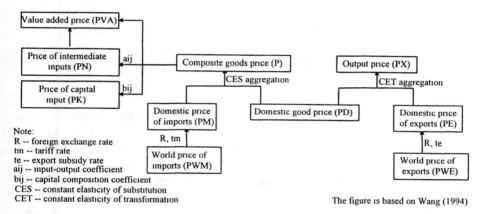

Figure 3.5 Price system

Table 3.2
Price equations

(1) $PM_i = (1+tm_i) \overline{PWM_i} \ \overline{R}$ (domestic price of import goods)

(2) $PE_i = (1-te_i) \overline{PWE_i} \ \overline{R}$ (domestic price of export goods)

(3) $PX_i = (PE_i E_i + PD_i XXD_i)/XD_i$ (average price of output)

(4) $P_i = (PM_i M_i + PD_i XXD_i)/X_i$ (price of composite goods)

(5) $PX_i XD_i + SUB_i = PVA_i XD_i + PX_i XD_i tc_i + XD_i \Sigma_{jp} a_{jp,i} P_{jp} + \Sigma_g PETAX_{g,i}$
$\quad\quad\quad\quad + \Sigma_g PACOST_{g,i}$ (activity cost composition)

(6) $PK_i = \Sigma_j P_j b_{j,i}$ (price for capital input)

(7) $PINDEX = GDPVA/RGDP$ (price index)

31

The world prices of imports and exports ($\overline{PWM_t}$ and $\overline{PWE_t}$) are exogenously fixed under the small country assumption.[5] The domestic prices of imports (PM_i) defined in equation (1) are the world prices in domestic currency ($\overline{PWM_t}$ $\overline{R}$) plus the tariff on a unit of imports. In this equation, $\overline{R}$ is the fixed foreign exchange rate and tm_i is the tariff rate on sector i. Similarly, the domestic prices of exports (PE_i) are defined in equation (2), where te_i is the export subsidy rate on sector i.

The prices of composite goods (P) and of sectoral output (PX) are defined in equations (3) and (4). In order to reflect the nature of imperfect substitutions between imported goods (M) and domestically produced goods (XXD), and between export (E) and domestic sales (XXD), the model adopts constant elasticity of substitution (CES) functions to define the two types of aggregated goods: composite goods (X) and sectoral output (XD). The composite goods (X) is the CES aggregation of imports (M) and domestic goods supplied to the domestic market (XXD) (see equation 12 in the trade block below). The sectoral output (XD) is the constant elasticity of transformation (CET) aggregation of exports (E) and domestic sales (XXD) (see equation 10).

Equation (5) shows the composition of production costs. The left-hand side of the equation is the total cash inflow of a sector, i.e., the product sales income plus the receipt of government subsidy. It is decomposed on the right-hand side into value added (PVA), indirect taxes (tc), spending on intermediate inputs (based on the fixed input-output coefficients $a_{jp,i}$), pollution emissions taxes, and pollution abatement costs. Pollution emission taxes ($PETAX_{g,i}$) and pollution abatement costs ($PACOST_{ia,i}$) are affected by pollution intensities, pollution cleanup rates, and prices. They are defined later in equations (36) and (37) in the pollution equation block. Equation (5) presents the relationships among various prices and tax rates. The price of intermediate inputs (PN) is implicitly defined in this equation via $PN_{ip} = \Sigma_{jp} a_{jp,i} P_{jp}$, ip=1,2, ... n.

Equation (6) defines the price of investment goods by sectors (PK_i). The coefficient b_{ji}, also called the capital composition coefficient, indicates the share of capital spending of sector i on investment good j. Because the composition of investment goods in one sector is rarely the same as the composition in another sector, the prices of investment goods are sectorally differentiated. The coefficient $b_{ia,i}$ for ia=1, 2, ... m, is zero because the pollution abatement sectors provide no goods for investment purposes. The last equation in the price block defines an aggregated price index

(PINDEX), which is equal to the GDP deflator (GDPVA) divided by the real GDP (RGDP).

The trade-related prices in the non-tradable sectors are set to zero, as well as the prices for trade-related terms in the pollution abatement sectors, because no pollution abatement services are assumed to be tradable.

Finally, the prices of the pollution abatement services (PX_i and P_i $i \in ia$) are defined in this block in the same way as the product prices.

(2) Output and factor inputs For simplicity, production is modeled in equation (8) by a Cobb-Douglas production function of two primary factors: capital (K) and labor (L):[6]

$$(8) \qquad XD_i = ad_i K_i^\beta L_i^\alpha$$

where, ad_i is the shift parameter in the Cobb-Douglas production function, α and β are share parameters for labor and capital, respectively, and $\alpha + \beta = 1$.

Such a production function indicates that only capital and labor are substitutable in a production process. The requirement for intermediate goods using fixed input-output coefficients is assumed always to be met. This is given later in the demand block (see equation 28 in Table 3.5).

To maximize profits, a firm uses capital and labor until the factor price equals the marginal product revenue:

$$\text{Factor price} = PVA \, \frac{\partial XD}{\partial F}$$

where $\partial XD/\partial F$ is the partial derivative of the production function in terms of factor F, $F = L$ or K. The demands for capital and labor under the Cobb-Douglas production function in the model, therefore, take the forms of:

(9') $wkdist_i \, WK = PVA_i \, \beta \, XD_i/K_i$
(9") $wldist_i \, WL = PVA_i \, \alpha \, XD_i/L_i$

The parameters $wkdist_i$ and $wldist_i$ in equations (9') and (9") are sectorally specific adjustment ratios for the prices of capital and labor respectively. These ratios are introduced because factor prices are hardly uniform across sectors. Using the sectoral adjustment ratios, the economy-wide average wage rate (WL) and capital return rate (WK) can be made sectorally specific. The adjustment ratios can be estimated by calibrating the model to a benchmark data set (for a detailed description, see section 5.4 of chapter 5).

The production behavior in the pollution abatement sectors is assumed to be the same as that in the production sectors. Therefore, the outputs (XD_{ia}) and factor demands (L_{ia} and K_{ia}) of the pollution abatement sectors are determined in the same way as for the production sectors and are included in the above equations.

As discussed earlier in section 3.2, pollution emissions or environmental quality degradation may reduce production or productivity. A simple way to represent the negative effects of pollution on production is to devalue the aggregate labor and fix the asset supplies in terms of the damage caused by pollution. For example, if environmental pollution causes an increase in the number of sick days taken by workers, the total effective labor-hours should be reduced in accordance with the seriousness of the environmental problem. The reduced labor and capital supplies can be represented in the factor clearing equations of the model closure block (block #7).

As suggested by Bergman (1993) and Gruver and Zeager (1994), pollution emissions or environmental quality indices can also be incorporated into production functions to capture the negative effects of pollution emissions on productivity. However, due to the lack of relevant quantitative studies, no attempts have been made to modify the production functions in this model in terms of pollution emissions.

(3) Trade block Table 3.3 lists the equations related to trade. As mentioned earlier, within each sector, domestic goods supplied to the domestic market and goods for trade are assumed to be differentiated and imperfectly substitutable. To handle the imperfect substitution, CES-type functions are often employed in CGE models.[7]

Table 3.3
Trade equations

---

(10) $X_i = ac_i \{\delta_i M_i^{-\rho c_i} + (1 - \delta_i) XXD_i^{-\rho c_i}\}^{-1/\rho c_i}$ (Armington function)

(11) $M_i = XXD_i \{(PD_i / PM_i)\delta_i / (1 - \delta_i)\}^{1/(1+\rho c_i)}$ (import demand)

(12) $XD_i = at_i \{\gamma_i E_i^{\rho t_i} + (1 - \gamma_i) XXD_i^{\rho t_i}\}^{1/\rho t_i}$ (CET function)

(13) $E_i = XXD_i \{(PE_i / PD_i)(1 - \gamma_i) / \gamma_i\}^{-1/(1-\rho t_i)}$ (export supply)

Equation (10) aggregates imports and domestic sales into a composite good using a CES function.[8] In this function, ac is the shift parameter, δ is the CES share parameter, and ρc is the CES exponent. The substitution elasticity (σ) in the CES function is related to ρc via the following relation: σ=1/(1+ρc). Similarly, the sectoral output (XD) is defined in equation (12) as a CET function combining exports and domestic sales of output. The CES and CET functions are different in the relation between exponent and substitution elasticity.[9]

The import demand (M) shown in equation (11) is derived by minimizing the costs of using the composite goods given in equation (4), subject to the CES function of equation (10), i.e.,

Minimize $\qquad P_i X_i = (PM_i\, M_i + PD_i\, XXD_i)$

Subject to $\qquad X_i = ac_i\{\delta_i\, M_i^{-\rho c_i} + (1-\delta_i)\, XXD_i^{-\rho c_i}\}^{-1/\rho c_i}$

Equation (11) indicates that an increase in the price of imports, relative to the price of domestic sales, will lead to a decrease in import demands.

Equation (13) derives the export supply (E) by maximizing the revenue from the given output defined in equation (3), under the constraint of the CET function in equation (12), i.e.,

Maximize $\qquad PX_i\, XD_i = (PE_i\, E_i + PD_i\, XXD_i)$

Subject to $\qquad XD_i = at_i\{\gamma_i\, E_i^{\rho t_i} + (1-\gamma_i)\, XXD_i^{\rho t_i}\}^{1/\rho t_i}$

The export supply function shows that the export supply increases when the price of exports, relative to the price of domestic sales, increases.

For non-tradable sectors and pollution abatement sectors, the corresponding trade terms are set to zero, and the sectoral outputs and sales of the composite goods equal that of domestically produced goods.

(4) Income and saving block Income, taxes, and savings of households, enterprises, and the government are defined by the equations in Table 3.4. These equations map the value added to incomes, to taxes, and to savings.

The total factor income (Y), defined in equation (14), is the sum of household labor income (YH) derived from equation (15) and enterprise capital earnings (YC) derived from equation (16).[10] Equations (17) and (18) define the household (YHTAX) and corporate (YCTAX) income taxes based on the tax rate on household income (t_{yh}) and the tax rate on depreciation (DEPR) minus exclusive corporate earnings (t_{yc}). Equation (19)

35

contains the total government tax revenue (GR). The total tariff, specified in the third term on the right-hand side of equation (19), is the sum of the nominal import $(PM_i M_i)$ multiplied by the tariff rate (tm_i). The fourth term on the right-hand side defines the total indirect tax, which is the sum of the nominal output $(PX_i XD_i)$ multiplied by the indirect tax rate (tc_i). Income taxes (YHTAX and YCTAX) as well as pollution taxes on production pollution emissions (ETAX) and household waste disposal (DTAX) are also included in the right-hand side of equation (19). The equations for ETAX and DTAX appear in the pollution block (block #6) below. The export subsidy (ESUB) is obtained as the sum of the value of the sectoral export outputs $(PE_i E_i)$ multiplied by the export subsidy rates (te_i) in equation (20).

Table 3.4
Income and saving equations

(14) $Y = YH + YC$	(total income)	
(15) $YH = \sum_i wldist_i\ WL\ L_i$	(household labor income)	
(16) $YC = \sum_i wkdist_i\ WK\ L_i$	(company's capital return)	
(17) $YHTAX = YH\ t_{yh}$	(personal income tax)	
(18) $YCTAX = (YC - DEPR)\ t_{yc}$	(corporate tax)	
(19) $GR = YCTAX + YHTAX + \sum_i PM_i\ M_i\ tm_i + \sum_i PX_i\ XD_i\ tc_i$		
$\quad +ETAX+DTAX$	(government tax revenue)	
(20) $ESUB = \sum_i PE_i\ E_i\ te_i$	(export subsidy)	
(21) $SG = GR - \sum_i P_i\ GD_i - ESUB - DSUB$	(government saving)	
(22) $SH = mps\ (YH\ (1-t_{yh}) + DCMP - DTAX)$	(household saving)	
(23) $SC = YC - DEPR - YCTAX$	(company saving)	
(24) $DEPR = \sum_i d_i\ PK_i\ K_i$	(depreciation)	
(25) $SAVING = SH + SC + SG + DEPR + FSAV$	(total saving)	

Government saving (SG), household saving (SH), enterprise saving (SC), and depreciation (DEPR) are given in equations (21) to (24), respectively. SG is the residual between the total government tax revenue (GR) and total government spending which is the sum of the government expenditure for final goods $(\sum_i P_i GD_i)$, the export subsidy (ESUB), and the pollution abatement subsidy (DSUB). The equation for DSUB is given in the pollution block (block #6) below. SH is derived from the post-tax household income $(YH(1-t_{yh}))$ plus the pollution compensation to the household (DCMP) less the household waste disposal tax (DTAX), multiplied by the fixed saving propensity (mps). SC equals the total capital income (YC) less depreciation (DEPR) and company income tax (YCTAX). Depreciation (DEPR), defined in equation (24), is the sum of the nominal values of fixed capital ($PK_i K_i$) multiplied by the depreciation rates (d_i) across sectors. Finally, total saving is defined in equation (25) as the sum of all saving terms above plus foreign saving (FSAV), the residual term in the balance of payment account defined in equation (50) in the model closure block.

(5) Demand block The demand for commodities can be divided into household consumption demand, government consumption demand, intermediate inputs, investment demand, and inventory. They are depicted by the equations in Table 3.5.

Table 3.5
Demand equations

---

(26) $P_i\, CD_i = \text{ß}h_i\, (YH\, (1-t_{yh})+DCMP-DTAX)(1-mps)$
$\qquad\qquad\qquad\qquad\qquad$ (household consumption)

(27) $GD_i = \text{ß}g_i\, \overline{GC}$ $\qquad\qquad$ (government consumption)

(28) $INT_{ip} = \Sigma_j\, a_{ip,j}\, XD_j$ $\qquad\quad$ (intermediate demand for goods)

(29) $INT_{ia} = \Sigma_j\, PACOST_{ia,j}\, /P_j$ $\quad$ (intermediate demand for cleanups)

(30) $DST_i = dstr_i\, XD_i$ $\qquad\qquad$ (inventory demand)

(31) $PK_{ip}\, DK_{ip} = \text{ß}k_{ip}\, (INVEST- \Sigma_i\, P_i\, DST_i - \overline{EINV}\,)$
$\qquad\qquad\qquad\qquad$ (nominal investment by sector of destination)

(32) $ID_{ip} = \Sigma_{jp}\, b_{ip,jp}\, DK_{jp}$ $\qquad$ (investment demand by sector of origin)

Household demand for each type of good (CD_i) in equation (26) is obtained by maximizing a Cobb-Douglas utility function subject to the household budget constraint. The solution to this optimization problem indicates that the demand in each sector is a fixed share of the total household disposable income, i.e., a fixed share of the household post-tax income minus household saving.[11] Similarly, government demand for good i (GD_i) is determined in equation (27), assuming a fixed share ($\text{ß}g_i$) of total government spending ($\overline{GC}$). The demand for intermediate goods (INT_{ip}) is derived in equation (28), based on Leontief's input-output coefficients ($a_{ip,j}$) and the sectoral output (XD_j). Equation (29) gives the demand for pollution cleanups (INT_{ia}), using pollution abatement costs ($PACOST_{ia,j}$) and prices of composite goods (P_j). Equation (30) contains the inventory demand of each sector (DST_i), under the assumption that the inventory demand for goods in a sector is a fixed proportion ($dstr_i$) of the sectoral output (XD_i).

Equations (31) and (32) depict the flows of the aggregated nominal fixed investment (excluding environmental investment) to the investment by sectors of origin (DK_i) and ultimately to the investment by sectors of destination (ID_i). The aggregated nominal fixed investment, on the right-hand side of equation (31), is the total investment (INVEST) minus expenditures for inventory ($\sum_i P_i DST_i$) and environmental protection activities ($\overline{EINV}$). The aggregated investment is allocated into production sectors of origin (DK_i) in equation (31), using fixed shares ($ßk_{ip}$). The investment demand by sector of destination (ID_i) is then determined in equation (32), based on the capital composition coefficients ($b_{ip,jp}$).

(6) Pollution block The prices and quantities of pollution abatement services were determined in the price and output blocks (blocks #1 and #2). The variables related to pollution taxes and pollution emissions still need to be calculated. Table 3.6 lists the equations defining the variables related to pollution and pollution control activities.

Similarly to equations (31) and (32), equations (33) and (34) draw the flow of environmental investment from the aggregate nominal fixed investment ($\overline{EINV}$) to investment demands by sector of destination (ID_i).

Equation (35) is a price conversion equation. To simplify the calculations in a CGE model, the initial prices of all products are usually set to one dollar. Thus, the unit of each product is equal to the amount of one dollar's worth of product in the base year. However, when measuring pollution, it is more convenient to use a unit such as the ton. Using the levels of pollution abatement in two unit systems in the base year, equation (35) converts the pollution abatement price of the one dollar's worth unit into dollars per ton.[12]

The pollution emission taxes ($PETAX_{g,i}$) and pollution abatement costs ($PACOST_{g,i}$) by sectors and by pollutants were introduced in the activity cost composition equation (equation 5 in Table 3.2). Equations (36) and (37) further define them. Equation (36) indicates that $PETAX_{g,i}$ is a function of the sectoral outputs (XD_i), pollution emission tax rates (tpe_g), pollution intensities ($d_{g,i}$), and pollution cleanup rates (CL_g). The right-hand side of the equation is equal to the total level of pollution emissions, i.e., $d_{g,i} XD_i (1-CL_g)$ multiplied by the pollution emissions tax rate (tpe_g). The pollution emission tax rate (tpe_g, g=1, 2, ..., m) is an exogenously determined policy variable in the unit of dollars per ton. The unit of pollution

38

intensity $(d_{g,i})$ is tons of pollutants per unit of one dollar's worth of output. Therefore, the unit of pollution intensity $(d_{g,i})$ multipliedby the output (XD) in real terms is tons. After multiplying by the pollution emission tax rate, the unit of the right-hand side becomes the dollar, which is the same as that of the left-hand side.

Table 3.6
Pollution equations

---

(33) $PK_{ia} \, DKE_{ia} = \text{ß}k_{ia} \, \overline{EINV}$
               (environ. investment by sector of destination)

(34) $IDE_{ip} = \Sigma_{ia} \, b_{ip,ia} \, DKE_{ia}$
               (environ. investment demand by sector of origin)

(35) $PA_g = (X0_g/TDA0_g) \, P_g$ (pollution abatement price conversion)

(36) $PETAX_{g,i} = tpe_g \, d_{g,i} \, XD_i \, (1 - CL_g) \, impl_{g,i}$
               (production pollution emission tax)

(37) $PACOST_{g,i} = PA_g \, d_{g,i} \, XD_i \, CL_g \, adj_{g,i}$ (pollution abatement cost)

(38) $TDA_g = X_g \, TDA0_g/X0_g$ (total pollution abated)

(39) $DA_g = TDA_g - GD_g \, TDA0_g/X0_g$ (production pollution abated)

(40) $CL_g = DA_g/\Sigma_i \, d_{g,i} \, XD_i$ (cleanup rate for production pollution)

(41) $DG_g = \Sigma_i \, d_{g,i} \, XD_i + \Sigma_i \, dc_{g,i} \, (CD_i + GD_i)$ (total pollution generated)

(42) $DE_g = DG_g - TDA_g$ (total pollution emitted)

(43) $ETAX = \Sigma_i \, \Sigma_g \, PETAX_{g,i}$ (production pollution emission tax)

(44) $DTAX = \Sigma_g \, tpd_g \, \Sigma_{ip} \, dc_{g,ip} \, CD_{ip}$ (consumption waste disposal tax)

(45) $DSUB = \Sigma_{ia} \, \overline{SUB}_{ia}$ (subsidy to pollution abatement)

(46) $DCMP = \Sigma_g \, \phi_g \, DE_g$ (environmental compensation)

Although While the model is calibrated to base-year observations, the initial data rarely fit this equation, usually because of the difficulty in collecting pollution taxes and because of measurement errors. There is frequently a discrepancy between the planned pollution emission tax and the actual tax collection, and it is often large in developing countries. For instance, the total amount of pollution emission taxes collected in China is only about half of what the Chinese government should collect based on pollution discharge fees standards.[13] To reflect the implementation difficulty, an adjustment factor $(impl_{g,i})$ is introduced into the equation. The unit less adjustment factor can be estimated by calibrating equation (36) to the base-year data. The sectorally specific factor can also take into account

39

the differentiation of pollution cleanup rates across sectors, which is otherwise ignored by using the economy-wide average cleanup rate (CL_g) in this model.

Equation (37) defines the pollution abatement costs ($PACOST_{g,i}$) by sectors and by pollutants. The costs are associated with the sectoral outputs (XD_i), pollution intensities ($d_{g,i}$), pollution cleaning rates (CL_g), and prices of pollution abatement services (PA_g). The abatement cost of a production sector is obtained from the amount of pollutants abated, i.e., $d_{g,i}XD_iCL_g$, multiplied by the price of pollution cleanup (PA_g) The units on both sides of the equation is the dollar.

Similarly to equation (36), while calibrating equation (37) to base-year observations, the problem of fitting the actual data to the equation arises because of measurement errors in the data and the use of an economy-wide average pollution cleanup rate. Again, a unit free adjustment factor ($adj_{g,i}$) is introduced into the equation to tackle this problem. The adjustment factor can be estimated by calibrating the equation to the data in the base year.

The output of a pollution abatement sector (XD_g or X_g, since $X_g=XD_g$), measured in the unit by which the unit price equals one dollar in the base year, was determined by the production function equation (equation 8) in the output block (block #2). In equation (38) the level of total pollution abatement (TDA_g), measured in the unit of tons, is converted from X_g using the initial values in both unit systems ($TDA0_g$ and $X0_g$). The total pollution abatement (TDA_g) consists of the pollution abatement of production sectors (DA_g) and government demand for pollution cleanups (GD_g) in final demand. Therefore, equation (39) determines the level of pollution abatement by production sectors (DA_g), which is equal to the total pollution abatement (TDA_g) less the converted government demand for pollution abatement products ($GD_gTDA0_g/X0_g$).

The average production pollution cleanup rate (CL_g) is defined in equation (40). It equals the level of total production pollution abatement (DA_g) divided by the total production pollution generation, where $d_{g,i}$ is a pollution intensity coefficient and XD_i is the output of sector i. The total levels of pollution generation (DG_g) and pollution emissions (DE_g) are given in equations (41) and (42), respectively. The total pollution generation (DG_g) comprises the pollution generated in both production processes and consumption processes, using production pollution coefficients ($d_{g,i}$) and consumption pollution coefficients ($dc_{g,i}$). Pollution emission is the difference between the level of pollution generation and the level of pollution abatement.

The taxes levied on production pollution emissions (ETAX) and on household waste disposal (DTAX) are defined in equations (43) and (44), respectively. The former is the sum of pollution emission taxes by pollutants and sectors. The latter is the sum of household waste disposal taxes across pollutants and sectors, based on household waste disposable tax rates (tpd_g) and the wastes from household consumption. In equation (44) $dc_{g,ip}$ is the pollution coefficient of household consumption.

The aggregate pollution abatement subsidy is the sum of government subsidies to pollution abatement sectors ($\overline{CSUB_{ia}}$), given in equation (45). The total value of environmental compensation (DCMP), defined in equation (46), is a linear function of the total amount of pollution emissions (DE_g), where ϕ_g is a fixed coefficient.

(7) Market clearing and model closure Under equilibrium requirements, the demand and supply for goods must be equal to each other, as must the demand and supply for factors.

Table 3.7
Market-clearing equations

---

(47) $X_i = CD_i + INT_i + GD_i + ID_i + IDE_i + DST_i$

(commodity equilibrium)

(48) $\sum_i L_i = \overline{LS}\,(1\text{-Runemp})$ (labor market equilibrium)

(49) $\sum_i K_i = \overline{KS}$ (capital market equilibrium)

(50) $\sum_i PM_i\,M_i = \sum_i PE_i\,E_i + FSAV$ (balance of payment)

(51) INVEST = SAVING   (saving-investment)

Equation (47) defines market-clearings for goods, in which the supply of the composite good in each sector must equal the aggregate demand. Equation (48) requires that the aggregate labor demand ($\sum_i L_i$) equal the exogenous labor supply ($\overline{LS}$) less unemployment, where Runemp represents the unemployment rate. There are two ways to close equation (48). One is to let labor be mobile and adjust labor demands (L_i) to fit the equation through a change in average wage (WL). Another is to set the wage rate rigid and make the unemployment rate endogenous to balance the equation. Capital market equilibrium is defined in equation (49).

41

The equilibrium of the pollution abatement sectors and the demands of those sectors for goods, labor, and capital are included in the above market-clearing conditions (equations 47-49).

The remaining two equations in Table 3.7 describe the macroeconomics closure for the balance of payments and the saving-investment relation. Equation (50) requires the balance of payment. The equation can be satisfied by either fixing the foreign exchange rate (R) and freeing foreign saving (FSAV), or vice versa. Equation (51) requires that the aggregate investment (INVEST) be equal to the aggregate saving (SAVING), which is defined in equation (25). This condition is often called 'neoclassical' closure in the CGE literature. A model containing such a condition is also called a 'saving driven' model.

Because the CGE model is based on the general equilibrium condition, the equilibrium equations are not all independent. According to Walras's Law, one of the equilibrium equations can be dropped without any effect on the simulation results of the model. The saving-investment equation is actually dropped from this model for that reason.

(8) Social welfare and GDP The model adopts a Cobb-Douglas utility function to measure social welfare (U) because the economy has only one representative household. To reflect the effects of pollution cleanup on social welfare, the social welfare function, shown in equation (52), includes the level of pollution abatement (TDA_g for $g=1, 2, \ldots, m$).

$$(52) \qquad U = \prod_i CD_i^{\beta h_i} \prod_g TDA_g^{\beta p_g}$$

Pollution abatement services are assumed to be public goods that are purchased by production sectors under environmental laws or regulations and/or by the government. Households have no demand for pollution abatement services.[14]

Finally, the nominal GDP (GDPVA) and real GDP (RGDP) are defined as:

$$(53) \qquad GDPVA = \sum_i PVA_i XD_i + \sum_i PX_i XD_i tc_i + \sum_i PM_i M_i tm_i + ETAX - ESUB$$
$$-CSUB - DSUB$$

$$(54) \qquad RGDP = \sum_i (CD_i + INT_i + GD_i + ID_i + IDE_i + DST_i + E_i) - \sum_i (1-tm_i) M_i$$

They are used in equation (7) to determine the price index.

In summary, this chapter presented the technical specification of an environmental CGE model. It began with a brief introduction to the environment-economy interactions and then illustrated the approaches of modeling the impacts of pollution and pollution control activities on production and consumption in a stylized two-sector model. The main part of this chapter was devoted to developing a multi-sector environmental CGE model designed for environmental policy analysis for developing countries. The proposed model incorporates pollution taxes, subsidies, and control activities into a standard CGE modeling framework for developing countries.

Because the various parameters in the environmental CGE model need to be specified, chapter 4 introduces the approach of numerical specification for the environmental CGE model.

Notes

1   The figure is based on Pearce and Turner (1990). Other figures the book, unless otherwise indicated, are made by the author.

2   For a description of these environmental protection instruments, see Pearce and Turner (1990).

3   These kinds of CGE models for developing countries were pioneered by, among others, Adelman and Robinson (1978), Taylor, et al. (1980), and Dervis, de Melo, and Robinson (1982).

4   For convenience, the notation adopted in the economic equations of the model is close to that used in Devarajan, Lewis, and Robinson's (1994) model. The layout and description of the equation blocks are also influenced by their work.

5   In 1992, China's total trade was only 2.2 per cent of the world trade (SSB, 1994). Therefore, this assumption is applied to China when the model is used for Chinese environmental policy analysis in chapters 5 and 6.

6   Other possible production specifications usually used in CGE models are single stage or nested CES production functions with the elasticity of substitution estimated separately.

7   See, for example, Dervis, de Melo, and Robinson (1982).

8   This kind of function is frequently called an Armington function, named after Armington's work (1969).

9   For a detailed discussion of the CES function, see, for example, Chiang (1967, pp. 416-419), or Devarajan, Lewis, and Robinson (1994, pp. 2-39).

10   This model assumes that household income is derived from labor income only, and that capital returns are retained in enterprises. This is true in a country like China, where financing markets are underdeveloped and most, if not all, capital is owned by the government and enterprises.

11   Other possible equations for household consumption are the linear expenditure system (LES) or the extended linear expenditure system (ELES) based on the Stone-Geary utility function. See, for example, Lluch, Powell, and Williams (1977) for discussions on the LES and the Stone-Geary function.

12   A detailed description of the unit of each variable in this model can be found in the GAMS program of the environmental CGE model for China in the Appendix.

13   See NEPA (1992).

14   This kind of assumption has been used by Robinson (1989).

4 Parameter estimation of the environmental CGE model

The environmental CGE model presented in chapter 3 contains various parameters. Correct estimation of these parameters is as important as correct model specification. This chapter introduces the approaches taken in parameterizing the model. Section 4.1 compares two parameter estimation approaches: the econometric approach and the calibration approach. It suggests that the latter is more suitable for CGE models for developing countries. Following a brief introduction to the social accounting matrix (SAM) in section 4.2, the framework of an environmentally extended social accounting matrix (ESAM) is outlined in section 4.3. The ESAM serves as a consistent environment-economy data set and is used to calibrate the environmental CGE model.

4.1   The econometric approach vs. the calibration approach

The econometric approach and the calibration approach are two alternative methods for the numerical specification of CGE models. They are distinguishable from each other, and each has advantages and disadvantages.[1]

The econometric approach, first implemented by Berndt and Jorgenson (1973) and Hudson and Jorgenson (1974), uses statistical methods to estimate the parameters of CGE models.[2] According to Lau (1984), the econometric approach is more sophisticated and satisfactory from a statistical point of view. The main advantage of the econometric approach is its implementation of statistical tests of the parameters. Each parameter derived from the econometric procedure is associated with a standard error and thus with a confidence interval.

However, there are limited implementation possibilities for the econometric approach. The approach is very demanding in terms of its re-

45

quirements for lengthy time series of equilibrium data sets. Mansur and Whalley (1984) noted that, for models of the scale usually being implemented, using the econometric approach to estimate jointly the entire group of parameters appears to be infeasible because of the lack of degree of freedom. To get around the problem, advocates of the econometric approach usually divide CGE models into a hierarchy of submodels and then estimate the parameters of each submodel separately. The lack of time series data in most developing countries makes the application of the econometric approach almost impossible.

In contrast, the calibration approach is a simple, easily used method that is much less demanding of data. It involves determining parameter values using only one year of benchmark data. The calibration approach was first introduced by Johansen in 1960. It has been widely used in the field of CGE modeling since the 1970s.

The calibration approach usually has four steps. The first step is to construct a benchmark data set consistent with the CGE model under study. The second step is to extraneously determine the values of some parameters, particularly elasticities. The reason is that the limited number of data observations in one year permits computation of only some of the parameters in the model. The third step is to compute the values of the remaining unknown parameters by calibrating each equation in the model to the benchmark equilibrium data. How to calibrate the model to a benchmark observation has been discussed by various authors, among them, Devarajan, Lewis, and Robinson (1994), and Mansur and Whalley (1984). A detailed description of parameter computation using the calibration approach is provided in a case study of China in the next chapter. The last step in the procedure is to conduct a base run to examine the correctness of the numerical specifications. The base-run results using the initial data in the base year must be identical to the base-year equilibrium. If they are not, the model needs to be debugged and/or modified until it can replicate the base-year observations.

The advantages and disadvantages of the calibration approach are obvious. As described above, the advantages are mainly reflected in the approach's parsimony in data requirements and ease of computation. As for its disadvantages, the calibration approach has been attacked by its critics on the following grounds. First, the parameter values determined by the approach are deterministic in nature. No standard errors are assigned to the estimated values and thus no measure of the reliability of the parameters is available. Second, the results of a model parameterized by the calibration approach are highly sensitive to the year chosen as the benchmark equilibrium. Finally, as Lau (1984) points out, the approach has an under-identification problem, that is, an inability to determine all the parameters of the model based on only one-year equilibrium data. Therefore, a number of parameters, usually elasticities, have to be assigned extraneously. The greater the number of exogenous variables is, the more serious the under-identification problem is.

In spite of these disadvantages, the calibration approach has been very popular and has been applied in nearly all CGE applications for developing countries because of its limited data requirements and ease in computing unknown parameters, in comparison with the econometric approach. It has also been adopted for numerical specification of the environmental CGE model for China, which is presented in the next chapter.

The benchmark data used for calibrating a CGE model must be consistent with the model. According to Mansur and Whalley (1984), the consistency requirements specify that: '(1) demands equal supplies for all commodities; (2) non-positive profits are made in all industries; (3) all domestic agents have demands that satisfy their budget constraints; and (4) the economy is in zero external sector balance.' The social accounting matrix (SAM) satisfies these conditions and has been widely employed as a consistent data framework for the calibration approach. A brief review of the SAM approach is provided in the next section. The environmental extension to a SAM for calibrating the environmental CGE model is introduced in section 4.3.

4.2   A brief review of the SAM

The SAM approach has been widely used in national accounting and development economics since it emerged in the early 1960s. An established technique, the SAM captures disaggregated economic activities and their interactions in an economy. According to Keuning (1994), a SAM can be defined as 'the presentation of a sequence of accounts in a matrix that elaborates the interrelationships between economic flows (and stocks), by adopting in each account the most relevant statistical unit and classification of these units.' The roots of the SAM have been drawn from two traditions: the national income accounts and the input-output (I/O) model of structural interdependence of production in the economy (Pyatt and Roe, 1978). The development of the SAM was motivated by the need to combine input-output data and income distribution data in a unified framework. Its forma-

47

		Activities	Commodities	Factors	Enterprise	Household	Government	Capital Acct.	Rest of world	Total
		1	2	3	4	5	6	7	8	9
Activities	1		make matrix							total sales
Commodities	2	intermediate input				household consumption	government consumption	investment consumption	export to row	domestic sales
Factors	3	factor payment								total net VA
Enterprise	4			factor payment allocation matrix			production subsidies			corporate income
Household	5				transfer		household subsidies			total hh income
Government	6	indirect tax			corporate tax	income tax				government income
Capital Acct	7				enterprise saving and depreciation	household saving	government saving		saving by row	total saving
Rest of world	8		import from row					invest. to row		row income
Total	9	total cost	total absorption	total net VA	total enterprise expenditure	total household expenditure	total government expenditure	total investment	row expenditure	

Figure 4.1 A representative SAM framework

48

tion was greatly influenced by Sir Richard Stone in the 1960s and 1970s (Robinson, 1989).

The SAM is a square matrix consisting of a series of accounts for various agents. Compared with the input-output technique, which captures only sectoral interdependence in a detailed production account, the SAM further incorporates the interactions between production, income, consumption, and capital accumulation in an accounting framework. Each row represents the receipts of the corresponding agent, and each column represents the expenditures. As with any double-entry bookkeeping system, the corresponding row and column sums for any agent must be equal. This implies that: (1) costs exhaust revenues for products; (2) expenditures equal incomes for each actor in the model; and (3) demand equals supply for each commodity (Devarajan, Lewis, and Robinson 1994).

Figure 4.1 provides a representative SAM framework. As one can see, the SAM contains not only standard input-output parts, i.e., the relationship between production activities and commodities, in entries (2,1) and (1,2), but also information about factors of production, institutions, and so on. For example, entry (3,1) traces the flows of income from producing sectors to factors of production, and entries (4,3), (5,3) and (6,3) further allocate factor payments to the enterprise, household, and government sectors, respectively.[3]

Inconsistencies often arise in assembling a SAM using data from various sources. The inconsistency problem is sometimes due to variations in definitions among the different accounts, but, more often, it is due to measurement errors (Dervis, de Melo and Robinson, 1982). To construct a SAM, techniques that force consistent conditions on raw data are frequently needed. Dervis, de Melo, and Robinson (1982) provided step-by-step procedures for data adjustment. Wang (1994) introduced a quadratic programming approach to balance a SAM.

4.3   The framework of an environmentally extended SAM (ESAM)

To calibrate the environmental CGE model presented in the last chapter, a consistent equilibrium data set that includes relevant environmental data is needed. Although the SAM has significantly extended the multi-sectoral framework of the input-output table, it still falls short in representing elements such as pollutants, environmental quality, natural resources, and most of their interactions with economic activities in the real world. Neither the impacts of economic activities on the environment nor the constraints of

			Activities		Commodities		Effluent fees	Factors	
			production	abatement	goods	cleanup		labor	capital
			1	2	3	4	5	6	7
Activities	production	1			make matrix				
	abatement	2				cleanup supply			
Commodities	goods	3	intermediate input (use)						
	cleanup	4	payment (cost) for cleaning						
Pollution effluent fees		5	pollution emission tax						
Factors	labor	6							
	capital	7	factor payment						
	land	8							
Institutes	household	9						factor payment	
	enterprise	10						allocation matrix	
	government	11	indirect tax		tariff		transfer to government		
Consumption	goods	12							
	cleanup	13							
Subsidies to production sector		14							
Subsidies to pollution control		15							
Capital account		16							
Environmental investment		17							
Inventory		18							
Rest of the world (row)		19			import from row				
Total		20	total cost		total absorption		effluent fees	total net value-added	
Pollutants (in physical terms)		21	pollutants abated or reused						
Resources (in physical terms)		22	resource renewal						

Figure 4.2 Framework of an environmentally extended SAM

land	Institutes			Consumption		Production subsidies	Pollution control subsidies	Capital acct
	household	enterprise	government	goods	cleanup			
8	9	10	11	12	13	14	15	16
						production subsidies		
							pollution control subsidies	
				consumption & inventory				
	waste disposal payment							
		transfer to household	household subsidies					
	household income tax	corporate tax						
	household consumption		government consumption					investment consumption
	household purchase		government purchase					
			production subsidies					
			pollution control subsidies					
	household saving	depreciation and corporate saving	government saving					
								environmental investment
								inventory
								invest to row
	total household expenditure	total enterprise expenditure	total government expenditure	total consumption		production subsidy	environmental subsidy	total investment

Figure 4.2 (continued)

51

	Env. invest	Inventory	ROW	Total	Pollutants	Resources	Environment	
	17	18	19	20	21	22	23	
			export to row	total sales	pollution generated	resource consumption		1
					from production			2
				domestic sales				3
								4
				effluent fees				5
				total				6
				net value				7
				added				8
				household income				9
				corporate income				10
				government income				11
	environ. investment consumption	inventory		total consumption	consumption pollution			12
								13
				production subsidy				14
				environ. subsidy				15
			saving by row	total saving				16
				total environ. investment				17
				inventory				18
			residual	row income				19
	total environ. investment	inventory	row expenditure					20
							pollution emitted	21
							resource depleted	22

Figure 4.2 (continued)

environmental quality on production and welfare have been reflected directly in a SAM framework. This section extends the SAM to account for pollution-related activities. The main purpose of developing such a matrix is to have a consistent integrated accounting system for the numerical specification of the proposed environmental CGE model.

Economic activities have strong impacts on the environment, and vice versa. However, until recently, environmentally related data have been given little attention in national accounting systems.[4] For example, the widely adopted United Nations' system of national accounts (SNA) has long ignored the role of the environment.[5] To overcome that shortcoming, the United Nations introduced a revised SNA in 1993, and advocated compilation of special satellite accounts on the environment as a supplement to the central system (United Nations, 1993a, 1993b). In addition to the UN's work in revising the SNA, other studies on integrated environmental and economic accounting have been proposed.[6] More and more countries have committed themselves to building integrated environmental and economic accounts in their pursuit of sustainable development. However, no formal, practical and operational accounting system that comprehensively considers the relationship between an economy and the environment has been developed yet.

Studies on incorporating pollution emissions and environmental impacts into a SAM-based framework have also emerged recently. Keuning (1993) proposed an extended SAM, called the national accounting matrix including environmental accounts (NAMEA). NAMEA integrates economic accounts with accounts for pollutants and environmental impacts. In NAMEA, economic flows in monetary terms and pollution effects in physical terms are combined into a single information framework. Pollution emissions from production, consumption, and imports are presented in a pollution emission account and further allocated into a set of environmental themes. However, pollution cleanup activities and other environmental protection efforts are not specified in the framework.

In order to capture the relevant interactions between pollution and economic activities in detail and provide a consistent and integrated data framework for calibrating an environmental CGE model, the framework of the environmentally extended SAM (ESAM), developed by the author, is presented in Figure 4.2. The ESAM provides an integrated data system in which pollution-related information, such as that concerned with pollution abatement sectors, sectoral payments for pollution cleanup, pollution emission taxes, pollution control subsidies, and environmental investments are accounted for separately.

More specifically, pollution abatement activities, i.e., activities that remove pollution, are separately listed in the activity account. The intermediate inputs of the pollution abatement sectors are presented in sub-matrix (3,2) in the commodity by activity matrix, which follows Leontief's approach illustrated in his environmental I/O tables (1970).[7] Sub-matrix (2,4) in the activity by commodity matrix presents the amount of pollutants that are abated by pollution abatement sectors. The costs for removing pollution or the payments for pollution cleanup in production sectors are presented in matrix (4,1). Pollution effluent fees by pollutants are singled out in row 5, the activity entry of which contains the payments by production sectors for their pollution emissions and the household entry of which contains the household payments for waste disposal. These fees are paid to the government in entry (11,5) and then partially transferred to the production sectors as pollution control subsidies in the pollution control subsidy column (15,11) and partially distributed by the government to households as subsidies (9,11). The compensation by the production sectors to the households for the damage caused by production pollution is presented, together with other enterprise transfers to households, in entry (9,10). Government efforts in pollution abatement are also reflected in government spending on pollution cleanup in entry (13,11). Household spending on pollution cleanup, if there is any, appears in entry (13,9). Environmental investment is separately accounted for in the environmental investment column (column 17) and row (row 17) in order to distinguish environmental investment from other types of investment and, furthermore, environmental investment consumption from other types of consumption.

The flows of pollutants and resources in physical terms are also presented within the ESAM. Different from Keuning's approach of having the physical data of pollution emissions mixed with the monetary data in a SAM, the ESAM leaves pollutant and resource matrices outside the monetary SAM to keep the matrix consistent in monetary units. Pollution generated from both production and consumption processes is presented in the activity and consumption rows of the pollutant column, i.e., matrices (1,22) and (12,22), respectively. The levels of pollution abatement and reuse are shown in the activity column of the pollutant row, i.e., matrices (21,1) and (21,2).[8] The entry (21,23), i.e., the environment column at the end of the pollutant row (row 21), contains the amount of pollutants emitted into the environment. The flows of natural resource consumption and renewal as well as resource depletion in physical terms are presented in a similar way in the resource row (row 22) and column (column 22).

Following Keuning's approach in NAMEA, the flows of pollution discharge in an ESAM could be also traced by environmental themes, such as acid rain, eutrophication, and global warming, for measuring the environmental impacts of pollution emissions. Such themes are, however, omitted in the current table because of the difficulty in obtaining or estimating relevant data in most developing countries. In addition, an ESAM could also separate and explicitly specify the feedbacks of the environment on the economy, e.g., the negative effects of pollution emissions on production. But, because of the lack of sophisticated studies at the macro level, the effects of pollution on production are rather implicitly represented by production output in the matrix. The environment column (column 23) in the ESAM, therefore, only functions as a sink for pollution emissions and natural resource depletion. Its purpose is to keep the row sums of pollutants and the resource rows equal to their column sums in the SAM tradition.

A detailed discussion of how to calibrate a CGE model with a SAM is given by Devarajan, Lewis, and Robinson (1994). A numerical example of calibrating the environmental CGE model is provided in the next chapter in a case study using Chinese data.

In summary, this chapter has reviewed two approaches to the numerical specification of CGE models: the econometric approach and the calibration approach. The calibration approach is often used for CGE models of developing countries because of its limited data requirements and ease of parameter computation. To provide a consistent and integrated equilibrium data set for calibrating an environmental CGE model, this chapter has introduced the framework of the environmentally extended SAM (ESAM) model. In the ESAM model, pollution abatement activities are distinguished from production activities, and the pollutants removed are treated as special goods. In addition, pollution emission taxes, pollution control subsidies, and environmental investments are also accounted for separately.

The next chapter outlines the environmental CGE model of China. A numerical ESAM is constructed using Chinese data. The parameter specification of the environmental CGE model based on the ESAM is described in detail.

Notes

1   Mansur and Whalley (1984) and Lau (1984) compare these two approaches thoroughly.

2   Jorgenson (1984) provides a detailed description of this approach.

3   For a detailed description of the SAM, see Pyatt and Round (1985). Besides being an accounting system, the SAM is also a statistical basis for modeling in policy analysis, e.g., the multiplier analysis of a SAM model. For more description of SAM modeling, see Defourny and Thorbecke (1984) and Pyatt (1988).

4   Although the environmental extension of I/O accounts has been discussed since the late 1960s (for example, see Leontief, 1970), today, this concept is still primarily a theoretical framework.

5   Bartelmus et al. (1993) pointed out that the SNA fails to consider '(a) new scarcities of natural resources that could threaten the sustained production of the economy and (b) the degradation of environmental quality caused mainly by pollution and its effects on human health and welfare.'

6   See, for example, Ahmad et al. (1989) and Lutz (1993).

7   Quite a number of researchers have used Leontief's approach to describe intermediate flows of pollution abatement activities and pollution abated in I/O tables. See, among others, Idenburg and Steenge (1991).

8   Pollution reused includes the pollution produced in one production sector and taken for free as an input by another production sector.

Part Two
AN APPLICATION TO CHINA

5   An environmental CGE model for China

This chapter applies the environmental CGE model developed in chapter 3 to China. Section 5.1 briefly reviews the recent Chinese reforms and environmental problems. Section 5.2 reviews some CGE models of the Chinese economy, and section 5.3 presents the environmental CGE model of China. An ESAM using 1990 Chinese data is constructed in section 5.4. Parameter estimation through calibrating the CGE model to the ESAM is discussed in section 5.5. Section 5.6 conducts some sensitivity analyses of the model.

5.1   Country background

There are many reports on the Chinese economy and environmental problems.[1] This section only attempts to provide some minimal background information for the reader to better understand the environmental CGE model for China that is introduced in subsequent sections.

Moving toward a market-oriented economy

China began its well-known economic reform in 1978. In contrast to the 'big-bang' method used in the reforms of Eastern European countries, the Chinese economic reform has been gradual and step-by-step. It began by replacing the commune system with a household responsibility system in some rural areas. Incrementally, it has been reducing central planning and introducing market mechanisms into production, distribution, prices, and trade in the other economic sectors and spatially all over the country.

To reduce the shock from this economic transition, the Chinese government first adopted a 'two-tier plan/market' system in the late 1970s.[2] In the system, the allocation and prices of central planning and market mechanisms coexist as market rules gradually replace central planning. In the early 1990s, the government decided to fully engage in establishing a market economy. Building a well-functioning market economy was formally established as a national policy in the 14th national conference of the Chinese Communist Party in October 1992 and ratified by the 8th National People's Congress in March 1993. The Constitution of 1982 was also amended in 1993 to emphasize this policy.

Since 1978 the Chinese economy has undergone tremendous changes. From 1978 to 1993, the average growth rate of the GNP was over 9 per cent per annum. Besides the fast economic growth, the economy has moved significantly from a planned economy toward a market-oriented economy. After almost two decades of gradual economic reform, the number of prices controlled by the state, the quota of goods allocated under plans, and the production share of state-owned enterprises, as well as the importance of state investment financing, have all dramatically dropped. Moreover, most marginal resource allocation decisions are made at market prices instead of at planned prices (World Bank, 1992).

The latest studies of the Chinese economy (World Bank, 1993, 1994a, 1994b) show, in detail, that the market is playing a significant role in economic decision-making. According to the World Bank reports, the recent major achievements of the Chinese economic reform in transition to a market economy are as follows.[3]

1   Most prices are now determined by the market. In order to smooth price reforms, three types of prices (planned, guidance, and market prices) have been allowed to coexist since the early stage of price reform in 1985. The proportion of goods in total domestic retail trade that is subject to planned prices has fallen dramatically since then, in favor of market prices. The amount of goods subject to planned prices has dropped considerably further, with announcements in early 1993 of the relaxation of controls on prices of grains and edible oils. Along with this deepening of price reform, there has been a significant convergence between planned and market prices.

2   'The allocation of goods has moved progressively out of the mandatory plan. In 1980, 90 per cent of industrial goods and 837 production materials were allocated under the plan system. By 1993, the proportion of industrial goods under the plan had declined to less than 10 per cent and the number of production materials under the plan administered by the Ministry of Internal Trade (formerly called the Ministry of Materials and Equipment) was reduced to 13. At the same time,

consumer goods administered by the Ministry of Commerce declined in number from 274 in 1978 to 14 in 1993.'

3   Distribution systems and channels have diversified and expanded. China used to have a unified system to purchase and sell consumer goods. Sales are now made to private purchasing agencies or directly to consumers. New 'comprehensive' and 'specialized' distribution agencies have sprung up.

4   'Sophisticated forms of commodity markets for many agricultural products and industrial raw materials have been established.'

5   The market for foreign exchange has changed in terms of improving access and flexibility of use. China traditionally combined a nonconvertible currency with a rigid system of exchange control. In early 1994, China took a major step to unify its exchange rates and abolish the retention system in its foreign exchange regime. A market-based managed float is being established. These changes have considerably increased flexibility and reduced price distortions.

6   In conjunction with the above policies and real-side adjustments, the government is gradually establishing a legal framework for a market economy.

Generally speaking, the economic reform has significantly transformed the Chinese economy. Market mechanisms are becoming a dominant force in determining economic activities in China, which makes the economy suitable for the CGE approach. Of course, the Chinese economy still has a distance to go in order to become a well-functioning, free-market economy. The country still has rigid wage rates and strongly influences the prices and supplies of a certain proportion of key goods, for example.

Environmental problems and environmental control measurements

Although China is telling the world a story of successful economic development, its environment is showing a very different picture. Environmental degradation in China now is more pervasive and serious than ever before. According to the 1993 Environmental Communiqué of China (NEPA, 1994), air pollution was serious in large and medium cities and had worsened in small cities.[4] Among the surveyed 94 river sections running through urban areas, 65 (69 per cent) had been polluted. The quality of the groundwater had become worse, and groundwater subsidence caused by over-exploitation clearly occurred in 36 cities. Serious eutrophication was widely observed in lakes and near-shore seas, and red tides happened frequently. The forest coverage rate was only 12.98 per cent (1989 data),[5] and timber supply was still very tight. The soil erosion area expanded to 150 million hectares, or 15.6 per cent of the total land; one-third of the agricultural land was faced with significant soil erosion problems and 6.67 million hectare of agricultural land was exposed to industrial wastes and urban refuse. Finally, the number of rare and extinct animal species reached 312 and extinct plants 354. The latest data indicate that currently the annual environmental loss in China is worth nearly Y 100 billion.[6]

A 1992 World Bank report found that China's environmental condition even worse. About 60 per cent of China's city dwellers and about 86 per cent of its rural residents were estimated to have no access to safe drinking water. Average concentrations of suspended particles in the air of northern China cities ran more than five times the standard of the World Health Organization. Cultivation of semi-arid or sloping land had eroded almost 17 per cent of China's total land. Overgrazing had turned 30 per cent of China once extensive grassland into desert. The report said, 'The loss and degradation of ecosystem on this scale is a matter of immediate urgency and concern.'[7]

Although China's environmental problems are related to its natural setting and intrinsic problems,[8] the acute environmental degradation is largely attributed to environmental pressures from rapid economic growth and fast industrialization, poor pollution control techniques, and weak environmental management during the economic reforms.

In order to combat environmental problems, the Chinese government has been introducing a series of environmental policies and programs. The major environmental policies and regulations in use are environmental impact assessments for new or renovative large- and medium-scale projects, a pollution emission permits system (now on trial in some urban areas), pollution discharge fees, environmental standards (including pollution emissions standards and environmental quality standards), an environmental protection fund, and pollution source control subsidies. Recently, the Chinese government launched a five-year environmental protection program, that seeks to treat 80 per cent of all industrial wastewater and 88 per cent of all industrial waste gases by 1998.[9]

However, because of the lack of adequate quantitative models for environmental policy analysis, the overall effectiveness of these environmental policies and programs on pollution control and their economic implications are still unknown. There is a need for models to assess the environmental and economic impacts of such polices and programs. The existing CGE models of the Chinese economy are reviewed in the next section, and the environmental CGE model is developed in section 5.3.

5.2   A review of CGE models of the Chinese economy

The closer China moves toward a market economy, the more appropriate CGE models are to studying the Chinese economy. This section reviews, from a technical point of view, the CGE models that have been developed recently for the Chinese economy.

CGE models of the Chinese economy first emerged in the late 1980s.[10] Byrd (1987, 1989) introduced a stylized general equilibrium model representing the two-tier plan/market system in Chinese state-owned industry. In Byrd's model, each good can be distributed partly through the plan and partly through the market. Output plan targets and input allocations are modeled as minimum constraints on the flow of commodities from and to enterprises. Plan allocations of goods to final demand, consumption, and investment are minimum constraints on purchases of these goods by consumers and investors. Enterprises maximize profits, subject to the constraint that they must fulfill their output plan targets. Consumers are constrained in the consumption of planned goods and maximize their utility subject to their budget constraints. Production factors are fixed as are wage rates.

Byrd demonstrated that the model result is Pareto-optimal when no agents are constrained by plan targets. He indicated that the trend in China of gradually replacing plan targets and allocations with an increasing share of market transactions seems appropriate. Similar to Byrd's approach, Sicular (1988) introduced a stylized general equilibrium model of the mixed economic system in Chinese agriculture to analyze the interaction between planning and markets.

Based on the 1983 22-sector I/O data of China, Xu (1990, 1993) constructed an applied CGE model to study the effects of a 'big-bang' style economic reform on the Chinese economy and evaluate the degree of price distortion. Xu's model closely follows the CGE model of Cameroon by Benjamin, Devarajan, and Weiner (1989). Different from the Cameroon model, Xu's model includes the two-tier plan/market system of the Chinese economy. Each sector is divided into a planned part and a market part, and carries two prices: market prices and fixed planned prices, respectively. Unlike Byrd, who assumed a fixed quota for the planned consumption of each good, Xu assumed that the share of planned consumption of each good to total consumption is fixed. According to Garbaccio (1994), this assumption might be inconsistent with the Chinese planning process.

Martin (1990, 1993) used the CGE approach to review the roles of planning and markets in the Chinese economy, focusing on trade and the foreign exchange system. His CGE model has 24 sectors and takes into account the two-tier pricing system for domestic goods and the two-tier system for foreign exchange.[11] Martin's model follows the ORANI model of Australia.[12] It is short-run in nature, with an assumption of fixed capital in each sector. The crucial assumption is that economic agents respond to marginal market prices for inputs and outputs, rather than to official prices. The data source for the model is the World Bank's (1985) I/O table for 1981. To facilitate solution by Johansen's method, the model is linearized in percentage changes. This linearized specification means that the secondary redistributive effects of the differences between planned and market prices are ignored.[13] Martin's model highlights the effectiveness of exchange rate devaluation in stimulating trade expansion, raising efficiency, and strengthening the demand for labor. The results obtained from the model provide some useful policy insights, as well as numerical estimates not available without a formal model.

Garbaccio (1994) developed an 29-sector applied CGE model using the 1987 I/O data. The starting point of the model is the CGE model of the U.S. economy presented by Robinson, Kilkenny, and Hanson (1990). Following Byrd's work on the Chinese two-tier system, Garbaccio's model includes an explicit representation of the two-tier plan/market price system. The model separates state and non-state enterprises for most of the sectors. The differences between ownership types captured in the model include levels of participation in the government planning system, rates of taxation, access to factors of production, and total factor productivity. The reduced labor mobility that is a characteristic of Chinese state-owned enterprises is also modeled. The model has been used to analyze the sectoral effects of a number of policies for price and taxation reform.

To assess the impacts of economic integration among the three Chinese economies (mainland China, Taiwan, and Hong Kong) on the rest of the world, Wang (1994) developed a multi-region CGE model. The model divides the world into seven regions: Hong Kong, Taiwan, mainland China, Japan, U.S.A., the European Community, and the rest of the world. Each region has seven sectors and four production factors. The model is calibrated on a seven-region, six-sector SAM estimated for 1990. The data for the SAM are based on the global database for applied general equilibrium modeling developed by the Global Trade Analysis Project (GTAP) at Purdue University.[14] Wang conducted two sets of simulations. The first set reduces the international shipping costs between Taiwan and mainland China, and eliminates all tariffs among the three Chinese economies. The second set reduces bilateral tariffs among the assumed

Chinese Free Trade Area, Japan, and the United States by 50 per cent. The simulation results show that each Chinese economy will gain from greater integration by means of liberalization of trade and investment policies. Specifically, the opportunity cost of isolating the United States from East Asia is high for the three Chinese economies.

Ezaki and Ito (1993) and Chen (1994) also built their own CGE models of China. Chen's model is the first of this kind to be built in China. Chen also presented a ten-sector SAM using China's 1990 I/O data for the parameter calibration of his model.

These CGE models of the Chinese economy are still very much in the experimental stages, especially the early stylized models. In addition, no attention has been given to simulating Chinese environmental policy using a CGE model.

5.3   An environmental CGE model of the Chinese economy

Unlike the other CGE models of the Chinese economy, which tend to emphasize the 'two-tier plan/market system' (Byrd, 1985) by separating the prices and goods into market and planned categories, the model presented below does not attempt to specify the plan-related components explicitly. The reasons for ignoring the plan factors are that: (1) the deepening of economic reforms in recent years has significantly reduced the role of planned prices and goods; (2) economic decision making is now largely based on marginal profit or utility, which is determined by market prices rather than by planned prices; and (3) the model mainly focuses on environmental policy analysis instead of on the relationship between the plan and the market.

The model is static, neo-classical and saving-driven in nature, with fixed world prices. It has seven production sectors, which are aggregated from the standard 33 sectors used in China's I/O tables. The seven sectors are listed in Table 5.1.

Production factors include two primary factors, labor and capital, and intermediate inputs. Aggregate labor and capital supplies are exogenously determined. Sectoral labor and capital demands are determined from the profit-maximization condition that marginal revenue of product equals marginal factor return. Average wage rate is fixed to reflect the wage rigidity in China. Other exogenous variables include foreign exchange rate, government spending on consumption goods, government subsidy, and debt.

The model identifies three general types of pollution: wastewater, smog dust, and solid waste.[15] Thus, three corresponding pollution abatement sectors are included in the activity category.

Table 5.1
Sector classification in the CGE model for China

No.	7 sectors	In 33-sector I/O Table
1	Agriculture	01
2	Mining	02-05
3	Light industry	06-10
4	Energy industry	11-13
5	Heavy industry	14-24
6	Construction	25
7	Services	26-33

The model is presented in Table 5.2, and the endogenous variables, exogenous variables, and parameters are given in Table 5.3. Table 5.4 counts the numbers of equations and variables.

Table 5.2
The environmental CGE model for China

The economic part of this model is conventional, closely following the Cameroon models developed by Condon, Dahl and Devarajan (1986) and Devarajan, Lewis, and Robinson (1991). The model is unique how it combines pollution and environmental protection activities with economic activities.

The model includes the following environmental components:
costs (or payments by) to production sectors for pollution cleaning services,
pollution abatement activities,
pollution emission taxes on production sectors,
household waste disposal taxes,
environmental compensation by production sectors to households, and
separately accounted environmental investment.

The model contains:
n production sectors, of which s sectors export products and t sectors import goods;
m types of pollution and m corresponding pollution abatement sectors;
two primary factors: capital (K) and labor (L), and intermediate inputs;

Table 5.2 (continued)

---

one household group (h);
government (G); and the rest of the world (ROW).

Sets:
ip, jp =1, 2, ... n. (production sectors)
g, ia =1,2, ... m. (pollutants or pollution abatement sectors)
i, j =1,2,..., n, n+1, ..., n+m. (production and pollution abatement sectors)
ie =1,2, ... t. (sectors with exports)
im =1,2, ... s. (sectors with imports)
ic =1,2, ... k. (sectors providing goods for final consumption)

EQUATIONS

Prices: $4(n+m)+t+s+1$ equations

(1) $PE_i = (1+te_i) \overline{PWE_i} \ \overline{R}$ i ie (domestic price of export goods)

(2) $PM_i = (1+tm_i) \overline{PWM_i} \ \overline{R}$ i im (domestic price of import goods)

(3) $PX_i = (PE_i E_i + PD_i XXD_i)/XD_i$ (average price of output)

(4) $P_i = (PM_i M_i + PD_i XXD_i)/X_i$ (price of composite goods)

(5) $PX_i XD_i + SUB_i = PVA_i XD_i + PX_i XD_i \ tc_i + XD_i \Sigma_{jp} a_{jp,i} P_{jp}$
$\qquad + \Sigma_g PETAX_{g,i} + \Sigma_g PACOST_{g,i}$ (activity cost composition)

(6) $PK_i = \Sigma_j P_j b_{j,i}$ (price for capital input)

(7) $PINDEX = GDPVA/RGDP$ (price index)

Output, factor and trade: $5(n+m)+t+s$ equations

(8) $XD_i = ad_i K_i^{1-\alpha} L_i^{\alpha}$ (Cobb-Douglas production function)

(9') wldist$_i$ $\overline{L} = \alpha \ PVA_i XD_i/L_i$ (wage and labor demand)

(9") wkdist$_i$ WK $= (1-\alpha) PVA_i XD_i/K_i$ (capital return and capital demand)

(10) $X_i = ac_i \{\delta_i M_i^{-\rho c_i} + (1-\delta_i) XXD_i^{-\rho c_i}\}^{-1/\rho c_i}$ (Armington function)

(11) $M_i = XXD_i \{(PD_i/PM_i)\delta_i/(1-\delta_i)\}^{1/(1+\rho c_i)}$
$\qquad\qquad\qquad\qquad$ i im (import demand)

(12) $XD_i = at_i \{\gamma_i E_i^{\rho t_i} + (1-\gamma_i) XXD_i^{\rho t_i}\}^{1/\rho t_i}$ (CET function)

(13) $E_i = XXD_i \{(PE_i/PD_i)(1-\gamma_i)/\gamma_i\}^{-1/(1-\rho t_i)}$
$\qquad\qquad\qquad\qquad$ i ie (export supply)

Income, tax and saving: 15 equations

(14) $Y = YH + YC$ (total income)

(15) $YH = \Sigma_i$ wldist$_i \overline{L} L_i$ (household labor income)

67

Table 5.2 (continued)

(16) $YC = \sum_i wkdist_i\ WK\ K_i$ (company's capital return)

(17) $YCTAX = (YC - DEPR)\ t_{yc}$ (corporate revenue tax)

(18) $YHTAX = YC\ t_{yh}$ (personal income tax)

(19) $INDTAX = \sum_i PX_i\ XD_i\ tc_i$ (indirect tax)

(20) $TARIFF = \sum_{im} PM_{im}\ M_{im}\ tm_{im}$ (tariff)

(21) $GR = YCTAX+YHTAX+TARIFF+INDTAX+ETAX+DTAX+\overline{DDEBT}$

$\qquad +\overline{FDEBT}+\overline{DEFT}$ (government revenue)

(22) $ESUB = \sum_{ie} PE_{ie}\ E_{ie}\ te_{ie}$ (export subsidy)

(23) $CSUB = \sum_{ip} \overline{SUB}_{ip}$ (subsidy to production)

(24) $SG = GR - \overline{HSUB} - CSUB - DSUB - ESUB - \sum_i P_i\ GD_i$

$\qquad\qquad$ (government saving)

(25) $SH = mps\ (YH\ (1-t_{yh}) + \overline{REMIT} + DCMP - DTAX - \overline{DDEBT})$

$\qquad\qquad$ (household saving)

(26) $SC = YC - DEPR - YCTAX$ (company saving)

(27) $DEPR = \sum_i d_i\ PK_i\ K_i$ (depreciation)

(28) $SAVING = SH + SC + SG + DEPR - \overline{DEFT}$ (total saving)

Expenditures: $4(n+m) + 2n$ equations

(29) $P_i\ CD_i = ßh_i\ ((YH\ (1-t_{yh}) + \overline{REMIT} - \overline{DDEBT} + DCMP - DTAX)(1-mps)$

$\qquad +\overline{HSUB})$ (household consumption)

(30) $GD_i = ßg_i\ \overline{GC}$ (government consumption)

(31a) $INT_i = \sum_j a_{i,j}\ XD_j$ $\qquad i \quad ip$ (intermediate demand for goods)

(31b) $INT_i = \sum_j PACOST_{i,j}\ /P_i$

$\qquad\qquad\qquad i \quad ia$ (intermediate demand for pollution cleanup)

(32) $DST_i = dstr_i\ XD_i$ (inventory demand)

(33) $PK_{ip}\ DK_{ip} = ßk_{ip}\ (INVEST - \sum_i P_i\ DST_i - \overline{EINV} - BSPLUS)$

$\qquad\qquad$ 'ominal investment by sector of destination)

(34) $ID_{ip} = \sum_{jp} b_{ip,jp}\ DK_{jp}$ $\qquad$ (.ıvestment demand by sector of origin)

Pollution: $7m+n+2m(n+m)+4$ equations

(35) $PK_{ia}\ DKE_{ia} = ßk_{ia}\ \overline{EINV}$

$\qquad\qquad$ (environ. investment by sector of destination)

(36) $IDE_{ip} = \sum_{ia} b_{ip,ia}\ DKE_{ia}$

$\qquad\qquad$ (environ. investment demand by sector of origin)

(37) $PETAX_{g,i} = tpe_g\ d_{g,i}\ XD_i\ (1 - CL_g)\ impl_{g,i}$

$\qquad\qquad$ (production pollution emission tax)

(38) $PACOST_{g,i} = PA_g\ d_{g,i}\ XD_i\ CL_g\ adj_{g,i}$ (pollution abatement cost)

Table 5.2 (continued)

(39) $PA_g = (X0_g/TDA0_g) P_g$ (pollutant abatement price conversion)

(40) $TDA_g = X_g\, TDA0_g/X0_g$ (total pollution abated)

(41) $DA_g = TDA_g - GD_g\, TDA0_g/X0_g$ (production pollution abated)

(42) $CL_g = DA_g /\Sigma_i\, d_{g,i}\, XD_i$ (cleanup rate for production pollution)

(43) $DG_g = \Sigma_i\, d_{g,i}\, XD_i + \Sigma_i\, dc_{g,i}\, (CD_i + GD_i)$ (total pollution generated)

(44) $DE_g = DG_g - TDA_g$ (total pollution emitted)

(45) $ETAX = \Sigma_i\, \Sigma_g\, PETAX_{g,i}$ (production pollution emission tax)

(46) $DTAX = \Sigma_g\, tpd_g\, \Sigma_{ip}\, dc_{g,ip}\, CD_{ip}$ (consumption waste disposal tax)

(47) $DSUB = \Sigma_{ia}\, \overline{SUB}_{ta}$ (subsidy to pollution abatement)

(48) $DCMP = \Sigma_g\, \phi_g\, DE_g$ (environmental compensation)

<u>Market clearing:</u> (n+m) + 4 equations

(49) $X_i = CD_i + INT_i + GD_i + ID_i + IDE_i + DST_i$
                             (commodity equilibrium)

(50') $\Sigma_i\, L_i = \overline{LS}\,(1\text{-Runemp})$ (labor market equilibrium)

(50") $\Sigma_i\, K_i = \overline{KS}$ (capital market equilibrium)

(51) $\Sigma_{im}PM_{im}\, M_{im}+BSPLUS=\Sigma_{ie}PE_{ie}\, E_{ie}+ \overline{REMIT} + \overline{FDEBT}$
                             (balance of payment)

(52) INVEST = SAVING   (saving-investment)

<u>Social Welfare:</u> 3 equations

(53) $= \prod_{ic} CD_{ic}^{\beta h_{ic}} \prod_g TDA_g^{\,\beta p_g}$ (utility)

(54) $GDPVA=\Sigma_i PVA_i XD_i+INDTAX+ETAX+TARIFF-ESUB$
            $-CSUB-DSUB$ (nominal GDP)

(55) $RGDP=\Sigma_i(CD_i+INT_i+GD_i+ID_i+IDE_i+DST_i)+\Sigma_{ie}E_{ie}$
            $-\Sigma_{im}M_{im}(1\text{-}tm_{im})$ (real GNP)

Table 5.3
List of variables and parameters

Endogenous variables:

BSPLUS	surplus in balance of payment (curr Y 100 million)
CD_i	private consumption of product i ('90 Y 100 million)
CL_g	cleanup rate of pollutant g produced from production sector i (unitless)
CSUB	total subsidy to production sectors (curr Y 100 million)

Table 5.3 (continued)

DA_g	total amount of production pollutant g being abated (100 million tons)
DCMP	total environmental compensation (curr Y 100 million)
DE_g	total amount of pollutant g emitted (100 million tons)
DEPR	financial depreciation (curr Y 100 million)
DG_g	total amount of pollutant g being generated (100 million tons)
DKE_{ia}	environmental investment by sector of destination ('90 Y 100 million)
DK_{ip}	investment by sector of destination ('90 Y 100 million)
DST_i	inventory demand for product i ('90 Y 100 million)
DSUB	total subsidy to pollution abatement activities (curr Y 100 million)
DTAX	total household waste disposal tax (curr Y 100 million)
E_{ie}	export of products in sector i to row ('90 Y 100 million)
ESUB	total export subsidies (curr Y 100 million)
ETAX	total production pollution emission tax (curr Y 100 million)
GD_i	government consumption of product i ('90 Y 100 million)
GDPVA	nominal GDP (curr Y 100 million)
GR	government revenue (curr Y 100 million)
IDE_{ip}	environ. investment demand by sector of origin ('90 Y 100 million)
ID_{ip}	production investment demand by sector of origin ('90 Y 100 million)
INDTAX	indirect tax (curr Y 100 million)
INT_i	intermediate demand by sector of origin ('90 Y 100 million)
INVEST	total investment (curr Y 100 million)
K_i	capital demand by production sector i ('90 Y 100 million)
L_i	labor demand by production sector i (million workers)
M_{im}	imports from the rest of the world to the sector i ('90 Y 100 million)
$PACOST_{g,i}$	pollution abatement costs (curr Y 100 million)
PA_g	price of pollutant g abated (curr yuan/ton)
PD_i	domestic prices (unity)
PE_{ie}	domestic price of exports (unity)
$PETAX_{g,i}$	pollution emission taxes (curr Y 100 million)
P_i	price of composite good i (unity)
PINDEX	GDP deflator (unity)
PK_i	price of a unit of capital installed in sector i (unity)
PM_{im}	domestic price of imports (unity)
PVA_i	net or value added price (unity)
PX_i	average output price by sector i (unity)
RGDP	real GDP ('90 Y 100 million)
Runemp	unemployment rate (unitless)
SAVING	total saving (curr Y 100 million)
SC	company saving (curr Y 100 million)
SG	government saving (curr Y 100 million)

Table 5.3 (continued)

SH	household saving (curr Y 100 million)
TARIFF	tariff (curr Y 100 million)
TDA_g	total amount of pollutant g being abated (100 million tons)
U	utility (unitless)
WK	average capital return rate (unitless)
XD_i	domestic output by sector ('90 Y 100 million)
X_i	composite goods supply ('90 Y 100 million)
XXD_i	local sales of locally produced goods ('90 Y 100 million)
Y	total income (curr Y 100 million)
YC	company revenue (curr Y 100 million)
YCTAX	transfer of company revenue to government (curr Y 100 million)
YH	personal income (curr Y 100 million)
YHTAX	personal income tax (curr Y 100 million)

Exogenous or policy control variables:

$\overline{DDEBT}$	domestic debt (curr Y 100 million)
$\overline{DEFT}$	government deficit (curr Y 100 million)
$\overline{EINV}$	total investment in pollution abatement activities (curr Y 100 million)
$\overline{FDEBT}$	government borrowing from abroad (curr Y 100 million)
$\overline{GC}$	aggregate government spending ('90 Y 100 million)
$\overline{REMIT}$	net remittances from abroad (curr Y 100 million)
$\overline{HSUB}$	subsidy to household (curr Y 100 million)
$\overline{PWE}_{ie}$	world price of export product i (unity)
$\overline{PWM}_{im}$	world price of import product i (unity)
$\overline{KS}$	aggregate capital supply ('90 Y 100 million)
$\overline{LS}$	aggregate labor supply (million workers)
$\overline{R}$	foreign exchange rate ('90 yuan per '90 U.S. dollar)
$\overline{SUB}_i$	government subsidies to sectors i (curr Y 100 million)
$\overline{L}$	economy-wide average wage rate (curr Y 100 million/million workers)
mps	household saving rate (unitless)
tc_i	indirect tax rate on sector i (unitless)
te_{ie}	export subsidy rate on sector i (unitless)
tm_{im}	tariff rate on sector i (unitless)
tpd_g	tax rate on household waste disposal (curr yuan/ton)
tpe_g	tax rate on production pollution emission (curr yuan/ton)

Table 5.3 (continued)

t_{yc}	per cent of corporate revenue transferred to government (unitless)
t_{yh}	personal income tax rate (unitless)
ϕ_g	environ. compensation of a unit of pollutant emitted (curr yuan/ton)

Parameters:

ρc_i	Armington function exponent (unitless)
ρt_i	CET function exponent (unitless)
δ_i	Armington function share parameter (unitless)
γ_i	CET function share parameter (unitless)
η_i	export demand elasticity (unitless)
α_i	labor share parameter in a Cobb-Douglas function (unitless)
ac_i	Armington function shift parameter (unitless)
ad_i	Cobb-Douglas production function shift parameter (unitless)
a_{ij}	input-output technical coefficient ('90 yuan/'90 yuan)
at_i	CET function shift parameter (unitless)
b_{ij}	capital coefficient derived from capital composition matrix (unitless), $\Sigma_i b_{ij}=1$
$d_{g,i}$	production pollution intensity (ton/'90 yuan)
$dc_{g,i}$	consumption pollution intensity (ton/'90 yuan)
d_i	capital depreciation rate for sector i (unitless)
$dstr_i$	share of sectoral production for inventory demand (unitless)
$impl_{g,i}$	adjustment factor for the implementation of production pollution emission tax (unitless)
$adj_{g,i}$ (unitless)	adjustment factor for pollution abatement payment in sector i
βg_i	expenditure share of government spendings (unitless), $\Sigma_i \beta g_i=1$
βh_i	expenditure share of household spendings (unitless), $\Sigma_i \beta h_i=1$
βk_{ia}	share of environmental investment by sector of destination (unitless), $\Sigma_{ia}\beta k_{ia}=1$
βk_{ip}	share of investment by sector of destination (unitless), $\Sigma_{ip} \beta k_{ip}=1$
βp_g	exponent of total pollution abatement in utility function (unitless)
$wldist_i$	sector-specific parameter for wage of labor in sector i (unitless)
$wkdist_i$	sector-specific parameter for capital return rate in sector i (unitless)
$X0_g$	pollution abatement output in the base year ('90 Y 100 million)
$TDA0_g$	total level of pollution abatement in the base year (100 million tons)

The model contains 289 endogenous variables in total and 63 exogenous or policy control variables. These exogenous or policy control variables include various types of tax rates, subsidies, government expenditures, government borrowing, the average wage rate, and the foreign exchange rate.

Table 5.4
Numbers of equations and variables

	No. of equations	No. of variables
Price block	4(n+m)+t+s+1	5(n+m)+t+s+1
Output and trade block	5(n+m)+t+s	5(n+m)+t+s+2
Income block	15	17
Demand block	4(n+m)+2n	4(n+m)+2n
Pollution	2m(n+m)+7m+n+4	2m(n+m)+7m+n+4
Market clearing	(n+m)+4	
Utility and GDP	3	3

where:
n=7 (production sectors);
m=3 (pollution and pollution abatement sectors);
t=6 (export sectors); and s=4 (import sectors)

Total number of equations: 14(n+m)+2m(n+m)+3n+7m+2t+2s+27=289
Total number of variables: 14(n+m)+2m(n+m)+3n+7m+2t+2s+27=289

5.4   Compiling the ESAM of China

To calibrate the environmental CGE model of China, an ESAM needs to be assembled. This section constructs an ESAM using Chinese 1990 data. The ESAM contains the above three types of pollution and the three corresponding pollution abatement sectors.

Based on the existing 1990 I/O table and SAM of China, a seven-sector SAM, shown in Table 5.5, was constructed. The data, consisting of inter-mediate inputs, value added, and consumption in the SAM, were obtained by aggregating the 1990 33-sector I/O table compiled by the State Statistical Bureau of China (1993).[16] The data on trades, taxes, subsidies and debt come from a 1990 10-sector SAM made by Chen (1994).

Beginning with the 7-sector SAM, the ESAM was built by separating environmental activities from economic activities using the approaches described in section 4.3. The resulting 7-sector ESAM of China is shown in

Table 5.5
A social accounting matrix for China, 7-sectors, 1990

Unit: 100 million Yuan RMB in 1990 price				Activities Production sectors						
				Agri	Mining	Light	Energy	Heavy	Construct	Service
				1	2	3	4	5	6	7
Act.	Prod	Agri	1							
		Mining	2							
		Light	3							
		Energy	4							
		Heavy	5							
		Construct	6							
		Service	7							
Comm	Goods	Agri	8	1367.10	46.20	2191.30	0.90	342.10	16.30	169.30
		Mining	9	5.10	46.80	43.80	478.70	551.80	162.90	64.10
		Light	10	331.60	49.90	2332.20	21.50	736.60	98.70	591.50
		Energy	11	64.70	96.10	83.10	85.40	688.80	62.00	287.90
		Heavy	12	575.50	405.90	669.30	145.70	5776.30	1625.00	1001.30
		Construct	13	0.00	0.00	0.00	0.00	0.00	0.00	0.00
		Service	14	281.20	100.20	740.30	155.90	1019.40	215.10	1125.70
Value Added		Labor	15	4352.75	402.95	775.28	106.64	1427.75	620.18	2137.06
		Capital	16	470.01	146.69	585.36	185.19	1243.25	146.03	1367.79
		Deprecia.	17	124.00	139.17	230.22	126.03	534.62	64.00	743.72
Household			18							
Enterprise			19							
Government			20	88.00	67.00	558.00	181.00	580.00	38.00	93.00
Consump	Goods	Agri	21							
		Mining	22							
		Light	23							
		Energy	24							
		Heavy	25							
		Construct	26							
		Service	27							
Subsidy to production sectors			28							
Debts			29							
Deficit			30							
Capital Acct.			31							
Inventory			32							
Rest of World			33							
Total			34	7659.96	1500.90	8208.85	1486.96	12900.62	3048.21	7581.37

Table 5.5 (continued)

Commodities Goods							Value Added		
Agri	Mining	Light	Energy	Heavy	Construct	Service	Labor	Capital	Deprecia.
8	9	10	11	12	13	14	15	16	17
7275.96									
	993.90								
		7217.85							
			1408.96						
				11313.62					
					3048.21				
						7434.37			
							9822.61		
								4144.32	
10.00	10.00	83.00	0.00	56.00	0.00	0.00			
									1961.75
214	443	274	0	1620	0	0			
7499.96	1446.90	7574.85	1408.96	12989.62	3048.21	7434.37	9822.61	4144.32	1961.75

Table 5.5 (continued)

Household	Enterprise	Gov't	Consumption Goods						
			Agri	Mining	Light	Energy	Heavy	Construct	Service
18	19	20	21	22	23	24	25	26	27
			3366.76						
				93.70					
					3412.85				
						40.96			
							2790.62		
								3048.21	
									3796.57
		435.80							
0.00	1752.00								
3058.95		15.75							
87.52		0.00							
2678.92		173.30							
100.38		0.00							
937.59		95.16							
0.00		0.00							
1869.04		1642.14							
		579.00							
		-75.10							
1460.20	2392.32	899.55							
10192.61	4144.32	3765.60	3366.76	93.70	3412.85	40.96	2790.62	3048.21	3796.57

Table 5.5 (continued)

SubEnt	Debts	Deficit	Capital	Inventory	ROW	Total	
28	29	30	31	32	33	34	
0.00					384	7659.96	1
134.00					373	1500.90	2
134.00					857	8208.85	3
26.00					52	1486.96	4
285.00					1302	12900.62	5
0.00					0	3048.21	6
0.00					147	7581.37	7
						7499.96	8
						1446.90	9
						7574.85	10
						1408.96	11
						12989.62	12
						3048.21	13
						7434.37	14
						9822.61	15
						4144.32	16
						1961.75	17
	-75.10				9.30	10192.61	18
						4144.32	19
	110.00	139.60				3765.60	20
			127.95	161.05		3363.71	21
			0.00	6.18		93.70	22
			15.10	545.16		3412.49	23
			0.00	-59.42		40.96	24
			1454.97	268.21		2755.93	25
			2979.33	0.00		2979.33	26
			84.34	199.03		3794.55	27
						579.00	28
					110.00	34.90	29
						0.00	30
		-139.60				6574.22	31
			1120.21			1120.21	32
			683.32			3234.32	33
579.00	34.90	0.00	6465.22	1120.21	3234.30		34

Table 5.6
An environmentally extended SAM for China

Unit: 100 million Yuan RMB in current price, 1990				Activities Production sectors						
				Agri	Mining	Light	Energy	Heavy	Construct	Service
				1	2	3	4	5	6	7
Act.	Production	Agri	1							
		Mining	2							
		Light	3							
		Energy	4							
		Heavy	5							
		Construct	6							
		Service	7							
	Abatement	W.water	8							
		Smogdust	9							
		Solidwaste	10							
Comm.	Goods	Agri	11	1367.10	46.20	2191.30	0.90	342.10	16.30	169.30
		Mining	12	5.10	46.78	43.74	478.65	551.61	162.90	64.10
		Light	13	331.60	49.76	2332.05	21.30	736.04	98.70	591.50
		Energy	14	64.70	94.44	81.17	82.86	681.56	62.00	287.90
		Heavy	15	575.50	405.63	668.79	145.13	5774.52	1625.00	1001.30
		Construct	16	0.00	0.00	0.00	0.00	0.00	0.00	0.00
		Service	17	281.20	99.86	740.18	155.71	1018.76	215.10	1125.70
	Cleanup	W.water	18	0.00	1.14	3.47	1.95	11.77	0.00	0.00
		Smogdust	19	0.00	0.27	0.57	2.48	1.86	0.00	0.00
		Solidwaste	20	0.00	2.32	0.32	0.92	2.73	0.00	0.00
Pollution effluent fees		W.water	21	0.00	0.17	3.20	0.37	5.78	0.00	0.00
		Smogdust	22	0.00	0.08	0.62	0.14	1.40	0.00	0.00
		Solidwaste	23	0.00	0.02	0.07	0.06	0.16	0.00	0.00
Value Added		Labor	24	4352.75	402.35	774.63	105.98	1425.26	620.18	2137.06
		Capital	25	470.01	146.69	585.36	185.19	1243.25	146.03	1367.79
		Deprecia.	26	124.00	138.46	229.27	124.89	531.16	64.00	743.72
Household			27							
Enterprise			28							
Government			29	88.00	66.72	554.12	180.43	572.66	38.00	93.00
Consump.	Goods	Agri	30							
		Mining	31							
		Light	32							
		Energy	33							
		Heavy	34							
		Construct	35							
		Service	36							
	Cleanup	W.water	37							
		Smogdust	38							
		Solidwaste	39							
Subsidy to production sectors			40	0.00	-134.00	-134.00	-26.00	-285.00	0.00	0.00
Subsidy to pollution control			41							
Debts			42							
Deficit			43							
Capital Acct.			44							
Environmental investment			45							
Inventory			46							
Rest of World			47							
Total			48	7659.96	1366.90	8074.85	1460.96	12615.62	3048.21	7581.37

78

Table 5.6 (continued)

			Commodities							Pollution
Abatement sectors			Goods							
W.water	Smogdust	Solidwaste	Agri	Mining	Light	Energy	Heavy	Construct	Service	W.water
8	9	10	11	12	13	14	15	16	17	18
			7275.96							
				993.90						
					7217.85					
						1408.96				
							11313.62			
								3048.21		
									7434.37	
										18.33
0.00	0.00	0.00								
0.27	0.04	0.00								
0.60	0.20	0.24								
7.87	2.71	2.80								
2.24	0.61	0.27								
0.00	0.00	0.00								
0.41	0.05	0.83								
2.91	0.42	1.06								
0.00	0.00	0.00								
4.03	1.15	1.07								
0.00	0.00	0.00	10.00	10.00	83.00	0.00	56.00	0.00	0.00	
0.00	0.00	0.00								
			214	443	274	0	1620	0	0	
18.33	5.19	6.28	7499.96	1446.90	7574.85	1408.96	12989.62	3048.21	7434.37	18.33

Table 5.6 (continued)

		Pollution Effluent Fee			Value Added			Household	Enterprise
abated									
Smogdust	Solidwaste	W.water	Smogdust	Solidwaste	Labor	Capital	Deprecia.		
19	20	21	22	23	24	25	26	27	28
5.19									
	6.28								
					9822.61				0.59
						4144.32			
		9.52	2.24	0.31				0.00	1752.00
								3058.95	
								87.52	
								2678.92	
								100.38	
								937.59	
								0.00	
								1869.04	
								0.00	
								0.00	
								0.00	
							1961.75	*1460.79*	*2391.73*
5.19	6.28	9.52	2.24	0.31	9822.61	4144.32	1961.75	10193.20	4144.32

Table 5.6 (continued)

Gov't	Consumption							Pollution abated		
	Goods									
	Agri	Mining	Light	Energy	Heavy	Construct	Service	W.water	Smogdust	Solidwaste
29	30	31	32	33	34	35	36	37	38	39
	3366.76									
		93.70								
			3412.85							
				-40.96						
					2790.62					
						3048.21				
							3796.57			
								0.00		
									0.00	
										0.00
435.80										
15.75										
0.00										
173.30										
0.00										
95.16										
0.00										
1642.14										
0.00										
0.00										
0.00										
579.00										
-75.10										
899.55										
3765.60	3366.76	93.70	3412.85	40.96	2790.62	3048.21	3796.57	0.00	0.00	0.00

Table 5.6 (continued)

SubEnt	SubPC	Debts	Deficit	Capital	Environ. Investment	Inventory	ROW	Total	
40	41	42	43	44	45	46	47	48	
							384	7659.96	1
							373	1366.90	2
							857	8074.85	3
							52	1460.96	4
							1302	12615.62	5
							0	3048.21	6
							147	7581.37	7
								18.33	8
								5.19	9
								6.28	10
								7499.96	11
								1446.90	12
								7574.85	13
								1408.96	14
								12989.62	15
								3048.21	16
								7434.37	17
								18.33	18
								5.19	19
								6.28	20
								9.52	21
								2.24	22
								0.31	23
								9822.61	24
								4144.32	25
								1961.75	26
		-75.10					9.30	10193.20	27
								4144.32	28
		110.00	139.60					3765.60	29
				131.00	0.00	*161.05*		3366.76	30
				0.00	0.00	*6.18*		93.70	31
				14.00	1.47	*545.16*		3412.85	32
				0.00	0.00	*-59.42*		40.96	33
				1457.00	32.66	*268.21*		2790.62	34
				3048.21	0.00	0.00		3048.21	35
				86.35	0.00	*199.03*		3796.57	36
								0.00	37
								0.00	38
								0.00	39
								0.00	40
								0.00	41
							110.00	34.90	42
								0.00	43
			-139.60					6574.22	44
				34.13				34.13	45
				1120.21				1120.21	46
				683.32				3234.32	47
0.00	0.00	34.90	0.00	6574.22	34.13	1120.21	3234.30		48

Table 5.6. The sources of data or data estimation are briefly described below.

First, the pollution abatement sectors were separated from the existing seven production sectors in the activity account (columns 8-10 in Table 5.6). Pollution cleanups of pollution abatement sectors were treated as special goods and added into the commodity account (columns 18-20 in Table 5.6). Because I/O tables with pollution and pollution abatement sectors for China have not been built yet, it was difficult to compile the matrix of commodity by pollution abatement activity. According to the China's 1990 environmental annual report (NEPA, 1991b), China reportedly spent Y 1.83 billion in 1990 on operating wastewater treatment facilities. The total operating costs (or outputs) of the smog-dust and solid-waste abatement sectors at the national level and the disaggregated expenditure of pollution abatement sectors on intermediate inputs, however, were not reported in national statistical reports. An indirect approach was therefore adopted to estimate these outputs.[17]

The approach assumes that a known ratio of wastewater abatement output for a particular city to national wastewater abatement output equals the ratios for smog dust and solid waste abatement activities. With the ratios, the national outputs of the smog-dust and solid-waste abatement sectors can be estimated from the city's data. Since 1982, the Chinese city of Tianjin has been experimenting with building city-wide economic and environmental I/O tables.[18] Tianjin's tables provide the total outputs of the three pollution abatement sectors of the city. Using the city outputs of pollution abatement sectors and the ratio of city wastewater abatement output to national wastewater abatement output (which is available from existing data), the national outputs of the smog-dust and solid-waste abatement sectors were estimated. To estimate the intermediate inputs and value-added terms of pollution abatement activities at the national level, the corresponding technical coefficients in the 1987 Tianjin I/O table were used under the assumption that the coefficients would be the same as the national coefficients in 1990.

After separating the three pollution abatement activities from the seven production activities, the table further shows the spending of production sectors on the treatment of wastewater, smog dust, and solid waste in the pollution cleanup by production activity matrix. The matrix reflects the payments made by production sectors for pollution abatement services. Again, the pollution abatement cost to (or payments by) each production sector for each pollutant is not available in such a disaggregated way. Each was estimated by disaggregating the total output of each pollution abatement sector using the share of pollution generation by sectors. The underlying assumption is that the unit cost and the pollution cleanup rate of abating each type of pollution over seven production sectors are the same.[19]

Another pollution-related expenditure for production activities is payments for pollution emission taxes. The cost is presented in the pollution effluent fee entry of the production activity column. China has imposed taxes on pollution emissions since the late 1970s. The total collection of pollution discharge fees in 1990 was Y 1.737 billion. 0.936 was collected for wastewater emissions, 0.451 for waste gas emissions, and 0.289 for solid-waste dumping (NEPA, 1991b).[20] The pollution discharge fees at the national level were disaggregated by eight ownership categories,[21] and fitted into seven sector categories. The pollution discharge fees are collected by the government. According to relevant pollution effluent fee regulations, 80 per cent of pollution emission taxes are reinvested in pollution control activities, and the remaining portion is used to cover the overhead cost of environmental administrative bodies at various governmental levels.[22] In addition, 0.059 billion yuan was reportedly used for compensating pollution damage in 1990 (NEPA, 1991b). This amount of money is assumed to be transferred from enterprises to households, and, therefore, appears in the enterprise entry of the household row.

According to a Chinese EPA report on environmental investment (Zhang, 1992), the total investment related to environmental protection in 1990 was 10.9 billion yuan.[23] The investment in pollution abatement is transferred to production sectors as investment consumption demands in the consumption rows (rows 30-39 in Table 5.6) of the environmental investment column (column 45 in Table 5.6).

It is likely that part of the government spending and environmental investment is used to subsidize pollution abatement sectors or facilities, or used equivalently as government purchases of pollution cleanup. However, it was difficult to single out either one, given the existing statistical data. The government subsidies to the pollution abatement sectors (rows 8-10, column 41) and government spending on pollution cleanups (rows 37-39, column 29) are assumed to be zero in the table.

The levels of pollution generated from production and consumption processes are shown in the activity rows (rows 1-7) and the consumption rows (rows 30-36) of the pollutant columns (columns 49-51) in physical terms. They were estimated by multiplying the sectoral output by the pollution intensity. The pollution intensities of each pollutant by sectors were calculated using the data on the sectoral outputs and on the pollution generated in 82 Chinese cities, which are available in the 1990 environmental annual report (NEPA, 1991b). The aggregated levels of pollution generation by pollutants are different from the data reported in China's statistical yearbooks. One major reason for the discrepancy is that the intensities were derived from large- and medium-scale state-owned enterprises in 82 Chinese cities and underrepresent the reality of the entire nation.

The pollutant and resource rows (rows 49-52) and resource column (column 52) are blank because there was no sectoral data available at the time.

Before the ESAM is used, two potential problems are worth mentioning. First, the 1990 seven-sector ESAM acts much more like an example matrix for conducting a stylized policy analysis because of its highly aggregated data and rigid assumptions in estimating environmental data. With in-depth data collection and surveys, however, an applied ESAM for China can be built.[24] An applied ESAM will be very useful in modeling Chinese environmental policy analysis. Second, as Chen (1994) noted, in 1990 China had unusually high inventory demands, a high trade surplus, and a low growth rate relative to those in most years since 1978. Therefore, the 1990 data may not be representative of the economic performance in years with high economic growth.

5.5   Numerical specification of the Chinese model and initial values

This section uses the calibration approach discussed in chapter 4 to estimate the parameters of the environmental CGE model. The model is calibrated to the 1990 ESAM of China so that it can exactly replicate the economy represented in that ESAM. The approaches used in the parameter estimation are described below in the order of equation blocks. More detailed information about the procedure of parameter estimation can be found in the GAMS program listing of the model in the appendix.

To simplify the calibration and interpretation of results, a common practice in calibrating CGE models is to assume that the base year of the model is also the base year for all price indices. Because a CGE model handles relative prices rather than absolute prices, it is convenient to have all physical units defined such that all prices equal one. This approach also implies that sectoral flows in the SAM measure both real and nominal magnitudes. Thus, the initial goods market equilibrium will occur at all product prices equal to one (Devarajan, Lewis, and Robinson, 1994).

Table 5.7
Parameter specification of the environmental CGE model for China

	Agriculture	Mining	Light ind	Energy	Heavy ind.	Construction	Services	Wastewater	Smog dust	Solid waste
Output and Factor Block										
Labor	341.77	13.13	28.52	3.68	51.64	24.61	104.05	0.11	0.02	0.04
Capital asset	2480.00	1546.28	3288.79	1465.41	7128.28	1280.00	13047.72	53.70	15.35	14.29
wldist	0.7359	1.7706	1.5694	1.6640	1.5946	1.4561	1.1868	1.5948	1.5948	1.5948
wkdist	1.1893	0.9157	1.2300	1.0507	1.2360	0.8148	0.8036	0.3724	0.3724	0.3724
alpha	0.8799	0.5884	0.4888	0.2580	0.4477	0.7470	0.5030	0.4194	0.2682	0.4983
ad	17.6660	14.6248	24.9949	4.6729	16.0714	45.5822	6.6019	4.6623	2.1561	8.3814
Trade Block										
Armington elas.	2.0000	0.7500	0.7500	n/a	0.5000	n/a	n/a	n/a	n/a	n/a
rhoc	-0.5000	0.3330	0.3330	n/a	1.0000	n/a	n/a	n/a	n/a	n/a
delta	0.1460	0.254	0.013	n/a	0.02	n/a	n/a	n/a	n/a	n/a
ac	1.3350	1.8260	1.1300	n/a	1.2860	n/a	n/a	n/a	n/a	n/a
CET elasticity	2.0000	1.1000	1.1000	0.5000	0.9000	n/a	0.5000	n/a	n/a	n/a
rhot	1.5	1.909	1.909	3	2.111	n/a	3	n/a	n/a	n/a
gamma	0.813	0.709	0.874	0.999	0.917	n/a	1	n/a	n/a	n/a
at	3.113	2.222	3.123	9.246	3.443	n/a	13.857	n/a	n/a	n/a
Sectoral Tax Rates										
tc	0.0115	0.0488	0.0686	0.1235	0.0454	0.0125	0.0123	0.0000	0.0000	0.0000
tm	0.0467	0.0226	0.3029	0.0000	0.0346	0.0000	0.0000	0.0000	0.0000	0.0000
te	0	0	0	0	0	0	0	0	0	0
Demand Block										
BETAh	0.3503	0.0100	0.3068	0.0115	0.1074	0.0000	0.2140	0.0000	0.0000	0.0000
BETAg	0.0082	0.0000	0.0900	0.0000	0.0494	0.0000	0.8525	0.0000	0.0000	0.0000
DSTR	0.0210	0.0045	0.0675	-0.0407	0.0213	0.0000	0.0263	0.0000	0.0000	0.0000

Parameters in output and factor block

There are three groups of parameters in this block: the sector-specific ratios of production factors ($wldist_i$ and $wldist_i$), the share parameters (α_i), and the shift parameters (ad_i) in the Cobb-Douglas functions.

The number of laborers hired by the sectors (L_i) was obtained from China's statistical yearbook (SSB, 1991). Because data on fixed assets by sectors was not available,[25] the level of fixed assets of each sector (K_i) was estimated indirectly. Because the fixed asset of a sector is equal to the depreciation of the sector divided by the depreciation rate of the sector, fixed assets can be calculated based on depreciation and depreciation rates.[26] The sectoral depreciation is available in the 1990 China's I/O table, and the sectoral depreciation rate used in the study is obtained with minor adjustments, from China's statistical yearbooks.

Sectoral wage rates and the economy-wide average wage rate (WL) in 1990 were calculated by dividing the labor income given in the ESAM by the number of corresponding laborers hired. The 1990 average wage rate (WL) in China was Y 1,730 per worker. The sector-specific ratio of the wage rate ($wldist_i$) is defined as the ratio of the sectoral wage rate to the average wage rate. The use of sectoral-specific factors and a fixed average wage rate in the model reflects the wage rigidity and sectoral differentiation of wage rates in the Chinese economy.

The average capital return rate (WK) in 1990 was 0.2014 (depreciation rate included). The sectorally specific factors of capital return rates ($wkdist_i$) were calculated using a method similar to that used to derive $wldist_i$.

The shift and share parameters (α_i and ad_i) in the Cobb-Douglas production functions can be solved from equations (8) and (9'), using the initial values provided by or derived from the ESAM and the initial sectoral labor demands $L0_i$. For example, given $L0_i$ and the initial values of all terms in equation (9') available in the ESAM, α_i can be calculated via the following equation:

$$\alpha_i = (wldist_i \; WL \; L0_i)/PVA0_i/XD0_i$$

The terms $L0_i$, $PVA0_i$, and $XD0_i$ indicate the initial values of labor demand, value-added price, and sectoral output of sector i, respectively.

After finding α_i, the shift parameter ad_i in the Cobb-Douglas function can be calculated by substituting α_i and the initial values in equation (8), i.e.,

$$ad_i = XD_i / (L0_i^{\alpha_i} K0_i^{(1-\alpha_i)})$$

The values of these parameters in the output block are listed in Table 5.7.

Shift, share and elasticity in trade block

Four of the model's seven production sectors (agriculture, mining, light industry, and heavy industry) import goods from abroad. Those sectors, plus the energy and service sectors, also export goods.

The parameters in the trade block include the shift parameters, the share parameters, and the substitution elasticities in both the CET and Armington functions. Because of the under-identification problem of the calibration approach,[27] it is standard practice to estimate the elasticities outside the model. In this study, the substitution elasticities used in Garbaccio's (1994) CGE model for China were adopted for use. Because the relationships between substitution elasticities and the exponents in both the CET and Armington functions are known, the exponents pc_i and pt_i can be calculated directly from substitution elasticities, for example, $pc_i=1/\sigma_i-1$ in the Armington function. Using pc_i and the initial values of domestically produced goods ($XXD0_i$) and imports ($M0_i$) from the ESAM, the share parameter δ_i can be obtained by rewriting equation (11) as the following:

$$\frac{\delta_i}{(1-\delta_i)} = \frac{PM0_i}{PD0_i} (\frac{M0_i}{XXD0_i})^{(1+pc_i)}$$

The shift parameter ac_i can be calculated from equation (10) via the following formula:

$$ac_i = X0_i / \{\delta_i M0_i^{-pc_i} + (1-\delta_i) XXD0_i^{-pc_i}\}^{-1/pc_i}$$

The exponents (pt_i), the shift parameters (ac_i), and the share parameters (γ_i) of the CET functions can be derived from equations (12) and (13) in a similar way. The values of these parameters are presented in Table 5.7.

Tax rates and saving rate in income, tax and saving block

The tax rates and household saving rate were derived by calibrating the relevant equations to the base-year observations in the 1990 ESAM. The tax rates on household income and enterprise revenue are equal to the corresponding taxes in 1990 divided by the income or revenue, respectively. In 1990, the collection of private income tax was trivial and, hence, does not appear in the social accounting matrix. The calibrated income tax rate is therefore equal to zero. The average rate of enterprise capital earnings turned over to the government was 0.4428.

The sectoral indirect tax rate (tc_i) is the ratio of the indirect tax on each sector, shown in the activity column of the government row in the ESAM, to the sectoral output. Similarly, the tariff and export subsidy rates by sectors (tm_i and te_i) are the ratio of tariffs to imports and the ratio of export subsidies to exports, respectively. These tax rates are listed in Table 5.7. The household saving propensity was obtained by dividing total household saving by household post-tax income. It was 0.1497 in 1990.

Sectoral composition shares in demand block

The shares of household and government consumption by sectors (i.e., βh_i and βg_i) were estimated by dividing sectoral consumption by aggregate household and government consumption, respectively. They are shown in Table 5.7.

Following Leontief's definition exactly, the input-output coefficients, a_{ij}, i,j=1,2, ... 10, were defined in real terms as the intermediate input of sector j for good i of a unit output of sector j.

The share of sectoral production for inventory demand ($dstr_i$) is the ratio of sectoral spending on inventory demand to sectoral output.

The shares of investment by sector of destination (βk_i) were obtained from the 1990 investment data in China's statistical yearbooks. The capital composition coefficient b_{ij}, defined as units of composite good from sector i required to create one unit of capital in sector j, was usually derived from the capital composition matrix. That matrix shows the demands of each sector for capital goods from all commodity categories to fulfill the investment of the sector.

Given the frequent absence or poor quality of data for the capital composition matrix in many developing countries, estimating capital composition coefficients from the capital composition matrix is often impossible. To get around this problem, this study used the sectoral shares of aggregate investment to represent the shares of investment spending by sectors. This approach was suggested by Devarajan, Lewis, and Robinson (1994). However, as they pointed out, such a simplification assumes that capital investment in all sectors has the same structure as total investment, and, therefore, eliminates the possibility of affecting the pattern of final demand in the static CGE model through investment allocation. The input-output coefficients and capital composition coefficients can be found in the GAMS program listing of the model in the appendix.

Parameters in pollution block

The production pollution intensity coefficient (d_{gi}) is the level of pollution g generated from producing a unit of product i. The coefficients were estimated using the disaggregated pollution generation and output data from a survey of state-owned enterprises in 82 Chinese cities. The survey results were reported in the 1990 environmental annual report of the Chinese EPA (NEPA, 1991b). Similarly, the consumption pollution coefficient (dc_{gi}) is defined as the amount of pollutant g generated from consuming a unit of good i. In this study, dc_{gi} is assumed to equal d_{gi} because of the lack of pollution generation data from consumption.

The environmental compensation ratio (ϕ_g) in the environmental compensation equation represents the level of environmental compensation for a unit of pollution g emitted. It equals the reported total pollution compensation divided by the total pollution emitted. The environmental compensation data were obtained from the 1990 environmental annual report of China.

Other exogenous variables and key initial values

The unemployment rate in 1990 was assumed to be 4 per cent. The total labor supply is equal to the sum of workers by sectors plus the 4 per cent labor surplus. The aggregate capital asset is assumed to be fully utilized and, therefore, to equal the sum of fixed assets by sectors. The foreign exchange rate in 1990 was 4.78 yuan RMB for one U.S. dollar. The government spending, debt, and deficit are fixed and taken directly from the 1990 ESAM.

In 1982, the Chinese government established a system of pollutant discharge fees by introducing a set of levy standards on pollution discharge. In the system, 29 types of pollutants in wastewater, 21 in waste gas, and three groups of industrial solid waste are subject to discharge fees. Because wastewater and solid waste are two broad categories and include many types of pollution with different effluent fees, the tax rates on these two groups of pollution are set as the weighted average. The average tax rate for each category was calculated by weighting the tax rate on each type of pollution in the category by the share of pollution emissions in total pollution emissions. The average tax rates are 0.20 yuan per ton of wastewater and 3.00 yuan per ton of solid waste, respectively.

According to the effluent fee standards, China charges 3 yuan per ton of coal used in production sectors for the generation of smog dust. In 1990, China consumed 785.6 million tons of coal and generated 13.2 million tons of smog dust, i.e., burning 59.5 tons of coal to generate one ton of smog dust. The tax rate on smog dust was 178 yuan per ton. China did not tax household waste disposal in 1990.

The percentages of treated wastewater, smog dust and solid waste needed to meet the requirement of emission standards were obtained from China's 1990 environmental annual report (NEPA, 1991). In 1990, China produced 24.8 billion tons of industrial wastewater. Of that amount, 48.8 per cent exceeded the wastewater emission standards and required treatment. 64.7 per cent of that wastewater were actually treated, but only 57.8 per cent of the treated wastewater satisfied the wastewater discharge standards. So, the percentage of the treated wastewater that satisfied emission standards, out of the total standard-exceeding wastewater, was only 37.4 per cent in 1990. The percentages of smog dust and solid waste being treated to avoid effluent fee penalties were 73.8 per cent and 91.7 per cent, respectively, in 1990.

In addition, the aggregate investment in the three pollution abatement activities was Y 3.41 billion in 1990.[28] The exponents of wastewater, smog dust, and solid waste abatement in the social welfare function are arbitrarily set at 0.50, 0.25, and 0.25, respectively.

5.5   Sensitivity analyses

The parameters estimated in the previous section inevitably have errors or contain uncertainty. The errors or uncertainties further affect the policy simulation results of the model. The question now is how reliable the simulation results are, allowing for the errors or uncertainties in parameter estimation. To answer this question, sensitivity analyses were conducted to test the robustness of the simulation results to changes in the parameters.

According to Harrison et al. (1993), sensitivity analyses can be classified as conditional systematic sensitivity analyses (CSSA) and unconditional systematic sensitivity analyses (USSA). In a CSSA, the key parameters under study are disturbed one by one while the other parameters are held constant at their point estimates. In contrast, in a USSA, each

Table 5.8
Sensitivity analyses of the environmental CGE model for China

	Base	S1	SA1	% Change	SA2	% Change	SA3	% Change	SA4	% Change
Price index	0.99	0.99	0.99	0.0000%	0.99	0.0000%	0.99	0.0000%	0.99	0.0000%
Total output	41806.89	41713.91	41711.24	-0.0064%	41708.54	-0.0129%	41701.78	-0.0291%	41685.81	-0.0674%
Unemployment rate	4.00%	4.23%	4.24%	0.2364%	4.25%	0.4728%	4.26%	0.7092%	4.30%	1.6548%
Total income	15928.26	15892.49	15891.56	-0.0059%	15890.62	-0.0118%	15888.26	-0.0266%	15882.70	-0.0616%
Labor income	9822.32	9799.06	9798.45	-0.0062%	9797.82	-0.0127%	9796.26	-0.0286%	9792.57	-0.0662%
Government revenue	3700.98	3690.93	3690.50	-0.0117%	3690.06	-0.0236%	3688.97	-0.0531%	3686.38	-0.1233%
Government saving	899.43	889.48	889.05	-0.0483%	888.61	-0.0978%	887.53	-0.2192%	884.96	-0.5082%
Saving	6574.14	6554.24	6553.56	-0.0104%	6552.86	-0.0211%	6551.13	-0.0475%	6547.04	-0.1099%
Real GDP	17272.14	17227.29	17225.99	-0.0075%	17224.67	-0.0152%	17221.37	-0.0344%	17213.56	-0.0797%
Wastewater treatment	44.99	77.86	80.03	2.7871%	82.26	5.6512%	84.79	8.9006%	93.59	20.2029%
Wastewater discharge	237.27	203.82	205.12	0.6378%	206.22	1.1775%	202.85	-0.4759%	199.99	-1.8791%

Unit: 100 million yuan for monetary variables and 100 million tons for pollution variables

Base -- the results from the base year run

S1 -- raising the tax rate on wastewater discharge by 50%

SA1 -- increasing the wastewater intensity of light industry by 5%, other variables same as in S1

SA2 -- increasing the wastewater intensity of light industry by 10%, other variables same as in S1

SA3 -- increasing the wastewater intensity of heavy industry by 5%, other variables same as in S1

SA4 -- increasing the wastewater intensity of heavy industry by 10%, other variables same as in S1

% Change -- % change between the results from the sensitivity analysis scenarios and those from S1

parameter is assumed to be random with a distribution and all parameters are disturbed randomly and simultaneously based on their distribution. As Harrison et al. pointed out, 'a USSA is more complete and accurate than a CSSA, but at a severe cost in terms of the number of required solutions.'

In this study, the CSSA approach was adopted because of its parsimony in computation and lack of need for a large amount of prior information. It is common to test for substitution elasticities in the sensitivity analyses of many CGE applications. Because the focus of the environmental CGE model is on pollution rather than on trade, the sensitivity analyses for the environmental CGE model were conducted to test the robustness of the model solutions to changes in the parameters related to pollution. Of particular concern was the pollution intensity coefficients. As mentioned earlier, the pollution intensities were derived from the survey results of large- and medium-scale enterprises in 82 Chinese cities (NEPA, 1991b). Because the pollution intensity coefficients were determined in this way, they tend to underrepresent the pollution intensity because the village and township enterprises, many of which are technically backward and pollution-intensive and lack pollution control equipment, are left out of the survey.[29]

Table 5.8 reports the simulation results of increasing the effluent fee on wastewater discharge by 50 per cent (from 0.2 yuan/ton to 0.3 yuan/ton) in column 3, as well as the results of the same policy with changes in the wastewater intensity coefficients. For simplicity, the increases in the waste-water intensities of heavy industry and light industry, the largest and second largest industries in the Chinese economy, were tested in these sensitivity analyses. Following the approach of theconditional systematic sensitivity analyses, the two intensity coefficients were disturbed with increases of 5.0 per cent and 10.0 per cent, one at a time. The results from these simulations, as well as the percentage changes relative to the results assuming no error in the pollution intensity coefficients (in column 3) are shown in Table 5.8. The results indicate that the trends of the changes in outputs, incomes, employment, and pollution are consistent with those presented in column 3, although there were slight changes in the magnitudes of these variables. For example, the total production output, income, saving, and wastewater discharges all consistently dropped in each simulation in which the wastewater tax rate was raised by 50 per cent. In addition, the unemployment rates and levels of wastewater treatment rose in these simulations. These results indicate that the trends of variable changes are stable within the variation of the pollution intensities tested.

In summary, this chapter constructed an environmentally extended SAM using 1990 Chinese data and developed an environmental CGE model for China. The CGE model was calibrated to the environmental SAM for its parameter specification. Conditional systematic sensitivity analyses were conducted to test the robustness of the model in terms of the variations in pollution intensity coefficients. The results of the sensitivity analyses show that the model is stable, at least for the range of values in which the policy analyses occurred.

Notes

1   See, e.g., the World Bank reports (1992, 1993, 1994a, and 1994b) for the Chinese economy and Chinese economic reform, and Xie (1993) for a study on the environmental history and environmental policies of contemporary China.

2   See Byrd (1987) and Sicular (1988). The phrase of 'two-tier plan/market' system was used originally by Byrd.

3   The following summary is mainly based on a World Bank report (World Bank, 1994a).

4   For instance, the 1990 Human Development Report reported that 'deaths from lung cancer in Chinese cities are four to seven times the national average, with many of the deaths attributable to heavy air pollution from coal furnaces.'

5   The forest coverage rate increased to 13.9 per cent recently, according to Qu Geping, chairman of the Environmental Protection Committee of the National People Congress, on the second plenary meeting of the Eighth National People's Congress. See *People's Daily* (overseas edition), March 16, 1994.

6   See *People's Daily* (overseas edition), March 16, 1994.

7   See 'World Bank Assails China on Environment' by Robert Benjamin, in *Baltimore Morning Sun*, August 19, 1992, or the World Bank (1992).

8   The intrinsic problems include the huge population, low per-capita resource endowments, and the imbalance in resource distribution, as well as the environmental pressures from the long history of cultivation.

9   Other objectives include recycling half of the industrial solid waste, treating 80 per cent of the radioactive waste in urban areas, and

creating 77.6 million hectares of nature reserves (about 8 per cent of all land).

10   Garbaccio (1994) provided a brief survey of CGE models of the Chinese economy.

11   For a long time, Chinese foreign exchange rates were overestimated. To keep the foreign exchange market stable, China managed to implement two different foreign exchange rates. However, the two-tier foreign exchange system ended in 1994 after China devalued its currency in the middle of 1994.

12   See Dixon (1982) for an introduction to the ORANI model.

13   See Garbaccio (1994).

14   See Hertel and Tsigas (1993) for information about GTAP.

15   Wastewater and solid waste are rather broad and vague pollution categories. The reason for selecting them was that data on these two pollution categories were available in China's statistical reports.

16   The 1990 I/O table does not provide the activity-by-commodity matrix. The corresponding matrix in the SAM is a simple diagonal matrix; it assumes that each production sector does not produce side-products.

17   The Chinese EPA conducted a survey on environmental industries in 1995. The survey results, once they are availabe, may be able to provide more accurate information for this part.

18   Tianjin, the third largest city in China, is the only Chinese city that has built economic and environmental I/O tables. Its environmental I/O tables follow exactly Leontief's (1970) approach. Tianjin's 1982 I/O table has 80 sectors and 22 types of pollutants. The 1987 table is relatively small, with only 33 sectors and four types of pollutants. The city has also constructed a 1992 economic and environmental I/O table, which should be available by the time the research is done.

19   This estimation could be improved by conducting a survey on the spending of typical enterprises on pollution abatement activities.

20   In the ESAM, half of the 0.451 billion yuan waste gas emission tax is assumed to be collected by smog-dust emission fees. A more accurate number may be derived from the disaggregated pollution emission tax data available from the Chinese EPA.

21   The 1990 data were obtained during my visit to the Chinese EPA in the summer of 1994. The disaggregated data after 1990 have been published in China Environmental Yearbooks.

22   The Chinese regulation on the levying of a fee for pollutant discharge requires that up to 80 per cent of pollution discharge fee be used to finance pollution control activities and the remaining portion be used to cover the overhead costs of the environmental administrative bodies. A survey on the use of pollution discharge fees in several heavy industry sectors showed that close to 80 per cent of the fees were returned to the industrial sectors as a pollution abatement investment. See Zhang (1992).

23   The Y 10.9 billion investment includes not only the investment in pollution abatement activities but also investment in urban renewal and product renovation projects that are aimed mainly at improving environmental quality, e.g., projects for building central heating systems and projects for promoting the use of cleaner energy sources. According to a 1991 Chinese EPA report (NEPA, 1991b), only 41.7 per cent (4.54 billion yuan) of the environmental investment was directly invested in pollution abatement activities. Of that amount, 2.16, 1.47, and 0.51 billion yuan were spent on reducing wastewater, waste gas, and solid-waste discharges, respectively

24   Several ongoing surveys of Chinese economic and environmental protection activities can be very helpful in building a real ESAM for China. First, the China 1992 I/O tables, with 33 sectors and 117 sectors, was planned to be published in 1995. Second, the National EPA of China has conducted a survey of environmental industries in 1995. The survey results will reveal detailed data about pollution abatement sectors and other environmental protection activities. Third, the city of Tianjin city has been working on its 1992 economic and environmental I/O table. This survey of environmentally related data was conducted alone with the I/O survey this time, and the results would be better than in previous years. Finally, China just finished an inventory survey of the fixed capital stock of state-owned enterprises. The results may provide more closely related information for economic and environmental accounting.

25   China reports its fixed capital investment and cumulative fixed assets annually in its statistical yearbooks. However, the fixed asset data are not discounted.

26   This approach for estimating fixed assets was used by Garbaccio (1994) in his CGE model for the Chinese economy.

27   See the discussion in chapter 4 for details.

28   According to a Chinese EPA report, China spent 10.9 billion yuan on environmentally related investments in 1990. Of that amount, 3.41 billion yuan was directly spent on pollution abatement of the three types of pollution and was, therefore, listed separately in the ESAM. The rest was included in the general investment category.

29   The aggregate level of wastewater generation estimated using these pollution intensity coefficients was significantly lower than that reported in China's statistical yearbooks.

6 Chinese environmental policy simulations

China began to take actions against its pollution problem in the early 1970s. The major institutions and environmental policies in use now include an environmental impact assessment system, an industrial pollution effluent fee system, an environmental protection fund, pollution emission permits (now on trial in some urban areas), and other environmental management measures. In 1994, the Chinese government launched a five-year environmental protection program, with the goals of reducing industrial pollution by treating 80 per cent of all industrial wastewater and 88 per cent of industrial waste gases by the end of 1998.

This chapter simulates a series of environmental policy alternatives using the environmental CGE model for China. Among the three types of pollution identified in this model, wastewater is the most important to the natural environment of China and has received much attention from both the government and the public. As a result, the policy alternatives are focused on reducing wastewater discharges. Section 6.1 assesses the economic and environmental impacts of the pollution effluent fee system, particularly the scenarios of raising the tax rate on wastewater discharge. Section 6.2 describes simulations of pollution abatement subsidy policies. The economic impact of treating 80 per cent of all industrial wastewater, as required by the newly established five-year environmental program, is simulated in section 6.3. The household waste disposal taxation policy and the government purchase of pollution cleaning services are simulated in sections 6.4 and 6.5, respectively.

The types of policy simulations are not exhausted in this chapter. In fact, the environmental CGE model can be used for environmental policy analysis in a broader spectrum. The possibilities of using the model for other types of environmental policy simulations, including enhancing law enforcement in pollution emission taxation, adjusting investment allocation

Table 6.1
Selected results from pollution emission tax simulations

	unit	Base	S1-1	S1-2	S1-3	S1-4	S1-5
Total output	100 million yuan	41806.89	41802.15	41713.91	41699.45	41687.13	41676.56
Unemployment rate	percent	4.00%	4.02%	4.23%	4.28%	4.31%	4.34%
Price index	unit less	0.9908	0.9909	0.9911	0.9911	0.9912	0.9913
Total income	100 million yuan	15928.26	15924.93	15892.49	15885.74	15880.02	15875.12
Labor income	100 million yuan	9822.32	9820.34	9799.06	9794.82	9791.21	9788.13
Government revenue	100 million yuan	3700.98	3702.69	3690.93	3691.12	3691.24	3691.33
Government saving	100 million yuan	899.43	901.16	889.48	889.69	889.84	889.94
Investment	100 million yuan	6574.14	6574.87	6554.24	6552.52	6551.03	6549.73
Net foreign reserve	100 million yuan	683.25	682.52	679.14	678.10	677.21	676.45
Real GDP	100 million yuan	17272.14	17270.12	17227.29	17220.53	17214.77	17209.82
Percentage of industrial pollution under certain treatment to meet emission standards							
wastewater	percent	37.71%	37.41%	65.39%	68.34%	70.89%	73.09%
smog dust	percent	73.81%	73.82%	73.84%	73.85%	73.86%	73.87%
solid waste	percent	91.75%	91.78%	91.89%	91.91%	91.93%	91.95%
Total level of pollution abatement							
wastewater	100 million tons	44.99	44.62	77.86	81.35	84.36	86.96
smog dust	100 million tons	0.0599	0.0599	0.0599	0.0599	0.0599	0.0599
solid waste	100 million tons	6.0373	6.0373	6.0373	6.0373	6.0373	6.0373
Total level of pollution emissions							
wastewater	100 million tons	237.27	237.60	203.82	200.22	197.13	194.45
smog dust	100 million tons	0.0308	0.0308	0.0307	0.0307	0.0307	0.0307
solid waste	100 million tons	1.1160	1.1152	1.1043	1.1023	1.1006	1.0992
Emission tax	100 million yuan	12.02	14.45	10.41	12.14	13.56	14.76
Household waste tax	100 million yuan	0.00	0.00	0.00	0.00	0.00	0.00
Pollution subsidy	100 million yuan	0.00	0.00	0.00	0.00	0.00	0.00
Pollution compensation	100 million yuan	0.39	0.39	0.31	0.30	0.29	0.28
Utility		9.33	9.32	9.60	9.62	9.64	9.65

Note:

Base -- the base-year simulation

S1-1 -- raise the tax rate on wastewater by 25%

S1-2 -- raise the tax rate on wastewater by 50%

S1-3 -- raise the tax rate on wastewater by 100%

S1-4 -- raise the tax rate on wastewater by 150%

S1-5 -- raise the tax rate on wastewater by 200%

Other control variables in S1-1 to S1-5 same as

those in the base year

to be environmentally sound, and increasing environmental compensation ratios, as well as adjusting government and private consumption priorities toward clean products, are discussed in the next chapter.

6.1   Pollution emission taxes

The main focus of the Chinese environmental policy analyses is to examine the impacts (or effects) of alternative pollution effluent fees on pollution emissions and the Chinese economy.   China introduced a pollution levy system in the late 1970s.   By 1990, China had set up effluent fees on the emissions of about 100 types of pollutants in four pollution categories: wastewater, waste gases, solid waste, and noise.   The total pollution emission tax collected in 1990 was Y 1.75 billion.   By 1991, the tax had increased to Y 2.06 billion.   The pollution emission tax is a significant funding source for a special environmental protection fund that mainly invests in industrial pollution control activities.

Although the levy system has been praised as a successful means of raising funds for pollution control, it has weaknesses.[1]   One significant weakness is that the current fee is too low to give polluters an incentive to reduce their emissions.[2]   The need to raise the effluent fee has been discussed for years.   The question is by how much the fee should be raised and what the impact of the increase would be on the economy and pollution control.   Studies on this issue have apparently not yet appeared in the literature.

With pollution emission tax rates incorporated into the environmental CGE model, the model can be used to simulate the effects of increases in pollution effluent fees.   The average discharge fee on wastewater was chosen for these policy experiments.   The tax rate in 1990 was 0.20 yuan per ton.   It was assumed arbitrarily that the government raises the tax rate incrementally by 25, 50, 100, 150 and 200 per cent.   Changes in key variables, such as total output, income, employment, savings, price level, pollution abatement, and pollution emissions, are summarized in Table 6.1.

In general, as the tax rate goes up, the simulation results quantitatively show a steady decrease in production and a steady increase in the price index.   The decline in production further causes the unemployment rate to increase and the level of pollution generation to decrease.   The real gross domestic product (GDP) falls as well, following the decrease in the level of production.   The trends observed from the simulations agree with the pollution taxation theory of environmental economics.[3]

The simulation results also reveal more detailed sectoral changes in production and consumption, allowing a closer look at the impacts of pollution tax increases on each individual sector. Table 6.2 shows the changes in sectoral output.

Table 6.2
Sectoral changes in output
from raising wastewater emission tax rate

	Base	S1-1	S1-2	S1-3	S1-4	S1-5
Agriculture	7659.65	7658.15	7641.90	7638.68	7635.94	7633.60
Mining	1366.90	1366.77	1364.78	1364.44	1364.14	1363.89
Light ind.	8074.55	8072.47	8055.71	8051.90	8048.68	8045.92
Energy	1460.00	1460.80	1463.52	1463.66	1463.78	1463.88
Heavy ind.	12615.40	12614.57	12581.04	12576.42	12572.78	12569.08
Construction	3048.21	3048.90	3037.82	3037.17	3036.60	3036.10
Service	7581.20	7580.49	7569.13	7567.18	7565.52	7564.09

Unit: 100 million yuan

With the exception of that of the energy sector,[4] the production sector outputs drop when the tax rate on wastewater discharge increases. For example, when the tax rate is raised by 50 per cent, i.e., to 0.30 yuan per ton, the output of heavy industry drops by 0.27 per cent, or 3.44 billion yuan in absolute terms. Light industry output drops by 0.23 per cent, or 1.88 billion yuan in absolute terms. The negative impact on production is even present in non-polluting sectors, such as agriculture (a decrease of Y 1.78 billion or 0.23 per cent) and the service sectors (a decrease of Y 1.2 billion or 0.16 per cent).

Concerning the effectiveness of raising the tax rate on wastewater treatment, the simulations show that raising the tax rate by 25 per cent (to 0.25 yuan per ton) fails to reduce pollution emissions. In response to the tax rate increase, the industrial sector simply pays more taxes for its wastewater discharges. The total pollution emission tax revenue from the three types of pollution emissions increases from Y 1.20 billion in the base year to Y 1.45 billion.

When the tax rate is raised to 0.30 yuan per ton (a 50 per cent increase), the cleanup rate for industrial wastewater rises from 37.7 per cent (4.5 billion tons of wastewater treated) in the base year to 65.4 per cent (7.8 billion tons). Figure 6.2 plots the changes in the levels of wastewater treatment and wastewater discharge over the rise in the wastewater tax rate.

Note that the amount of wastewater decreases significantly after an increase of 50 per cent or more in the wastewater tax rate.

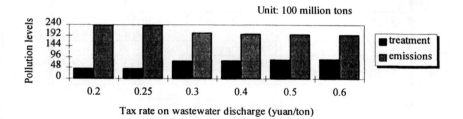

Unit: 100 million tons

Figure 6.1 Changes in wastewater treatment and emissions

In evaluating the simulation results, it should be noted that the model only measures the economic gain or loss from an environmental policy. No non-monetary environmental benefits from pollution reduction are captured. However, the results from the above simulations are useful to policy makers in evaluating the economic impacts and pollution reduction effects of pollution emission tax alternatives.

6.2   Subsidies for pollution abatement activities

Pollution subsidy is another popular method of pollution control. Different from taxation, a subsidy tends to result in a drop in the prices and an increase in the production levels of the sector receiving the subsidy. Again, the wastewater treatment sector is chosen for pollution subsidy policy simulations. Two subsidy scenarios were tested using the environmental CGE model. In the first scenario, a subsidy of 200 million yuan is assumed for the wastewater treatment sector; in the second scenario, the subsidy is increased to 400 million yuan.[5]

The primary results of the two subsidy scenarios are shown in columns 4 and 5 (S2-1 and S2-3) of Table 6.3. The price of wastewater cleanup falls by 10.3 per cent with the low subsidy and by 14.4 per cent with the high subsidy. The decrease in cleanup price brings about a decrease in pollution abatement costs to the production sectors and further reduces the product prices. However, the impact on product prices is very small in both scenarios and is not reflected in the price index. The level of wastewater

Table 6.3
Selected results from pollution control
subsidy simulations

	unit	Base	S2-1	S2-2
Total output	100 million yuan	41806.89	41805.95	41756.66
agriculture	100 million yuan	7659.65	7659.90	7651.29
mining	100 million yuan	1366.90	1367.00	1366.02
light industry	100 million yuan	8074.55	8075.03	8066.41
energy	100 million yuan	1460.00	1461.35	1463.23
heavy industry	100 million yuan	12615.40	12614.55	12595.07
construction	100 million yuan	3048.21	3047.04	3039.72
service	100 million yuan	7581.20	7581.17	7574.93
Unemployment rate	percent	4.00%	4.00%	4.11%
Price index	unitless	0.9908	0.9908	0.9908
Total income	100 million yuan	15928.26	15929.33	15912.71
Labor income	100 million yuan	9822.32	9822.82	9811.71
Government revenue	100 million yuan	3700.98	3700.88	3694.21
Government saving	100 million yuan	899.43	897.32	888.68
Investment	100 million yuan	6574.14	6572.40	6559.25
Net foreign reserve	100 million yuan	683.25	683.72	682.37
Real GDP	100 million yuan	17272.14	17271.44	17247.26
Percentage of treated industrial pollution to meet emission standards				
wastewater	percent	37.71%	39.53%	56.78%
smog dust	percent	73.81%	73.80%	73.81%
solid waste	percent	91.75%	91.75%	91.81%
Wastewater cleanup price	yuan/ton	0.4107	0.3683	0.3517
Total level of pollution abatement				
wastewater	100 million tons	44.99	47.16	67.68
smog dust	100 million tons	0.0599	0.0599	0.0599
solid waste	100 million tons	6.0373	6.0373	6.0373
Total level of pollution emissions				
wastewater	100 million tons	237.27	235.11	214.30
smog dust	100 million tons	0.0308	0.0308	0.0308
solid waste	100 million tons	1.1160	1.1164	1.1109
Emission tax	100 million yuan	12.02	11.75	9.11
Household waste tax	100 million yuan	0.00	0.00	0.00
Pollution subsidy	100 million yuan	0.00	2.00	4.00
Pollution compensation	100 million yuan	0.39	0.38	0.33
Utility	unitless	9.33	9.35	9.53

Note:

Base -- the baseyear simulation.

S2-1 -- subsidize wastewater treatment sector by 200 million yuan.

S2-2 -- subsidize wastewater treatment sector by 400 million yuan.

Other control variables in S2-1 and S2-2 same as those in the base year.

treatment is driven up by the increasing demand for wastewater treatment due to lower costs. The level of total wastewater treatment rises by 51.7 per cent (with a rise in the industrial wastewater cleanup rate from 37.7 per cent to 56.8 per cent) when a subsidy of Y 400 million is provided for the wastewater treatment sector.

Although the subsidies stimulate the production of the wastewater treatment sector, they negatively affect the total production output, given the limited capital resources available in the economy. The total output drops in both scenarios.

The two scenarios (Y 200 versus Y 400 million) differ in their impacts on output and income. The low subsidy scenario has a minor impact on the economy. Production output decreases very slightly, and the values of all variables are very close to their base-year values. The level of wastewater treatment increases slightly from 4.5 billion tons to 4.7 billion tons. The high subsidy scenario, however, causes production to decline. The unemployment rate rises from 4.00 per cent to 4.11 per cent, while income and savings fall.

Columns 4 and 5 of Table 6.3 show the detailed sectoral changes in production under two simulations. Compared with the base-year observations, subsidizing the pollution abatement sectors actually hurts some less-polluting or pollution-free sectors, decreasing, for example, the outputs of the agriculture and service sectors by Y 840 million and Y 630 million, respectively. The outputs of the pollution-intensive sectors, such as mining and energy, however, are not negatively affected. This is because all sectors are assumed to compete for capital resources under a tight capital supply constraint. When capital-intensive sectors, such as the energy and mining sectors, become more cost-benefit effective as a result of the decrease in their pollution abatement costs, they have the advantage of gaining more capital to increase their production.

6.3   An economic impact assessment of China's five-year environmental protection program

Facing the problem of serious environmental degradation, the Chinese government launched its five-year environmental protection program in the spring of 1994. The government hopes that the program will 'reduce industrial pollution, improve the urban environment and strengthen ecological environmental protection' within a five-year period.[6] Detailed environmental protection objectives are specified. Among other objectives,

Table 6.4
Selected results from other environmental policy simulations

	unit	Base	S3	S4-1	S4-2	S5-1	S5-2
Total output	100 million yuan	41806.89	41780.15	41773.17	41804.29	41807.02	41761.42
agriculture	100 million yuan	7659.65	7654.74	7649.23	7658.29	7659.94	7651.42
mining	100 million yuan	1366.90	1366.29	1366.47	1366.92	1367.02	1366.11
light industry	100 million yuan	8074.55	8069.51	8064.56	8073.21	8074.92	8066.69
energy	100 million yuan	1460.00	1461.83	1462.25	1461.12	1461.23	1462.90
heavy industry	100 million yuan	12615.40	12605.21	12607.29	12615.52	12615.11	12597.40
construction	100 million yuan	3048.21	3044.81	3048.05	3048.84	3047.51	3041.00
service	100 million yuan	7581.20	7577.76	7575.31	7580.50	7581.28	7575.49
Unemployment rate	percent	4.00%	4.07%	4.11%	4.02%	4.00%	4.10%
Price index	unitless	0.9908	0.9909	0.9909	0.9908	0.9908	0.9909
Total income	100 million yuan	15928.26	15918.48	15914.10	15926.88	15929.30	15913.62
Labor income	100 million yuan	9822.32	9815.90	9812.49	9821.29	9822.86	9812.41
Government revenue	100 million yuan	3700.98	3697.34	3703.34	3702.25	3701.64	3696.09
Government saving	100 million yuan	899.43	895.81	901.82	900.70	898.08	890.56
Investment	100 million yuan	6574.14	6567.83	6571.80	6574.84	6573.13	6561.33
Net foreign reserve	100 million yuan	683.25	682.24	681.39	683.01	683.32	682.26
Real GDP	100 million yuan	17272.14	17259.15	17253.82	17270.42	17274.04	17253.73
Percentage of industrial pollution under certain treatment to meet emission standards							
wastewater	percent	37.71%	46.24%	48.64%	38.58%	34.63%	46.14%
smog dust	percent	73.81%	73.82%	73.81%	73.81%	73.80%	73.81%
solid waste	percent	91.75%	91.79%	91.78%	91.75%	91.74%	91.81%
Wastewater cleanup price	yuan/ton	0.4107	0.4108	0.4108	0.4107	0.4107	0.4108
Total level of pollution abatement							
wastewater	100 million tons	44.99	55.14	58.00	46.03	46.19	64.74
smog dust	100 million tons	0.0599	0.0599	0.0599	0.0599	0.0599	0.0599
solid waste	100 million tons	6.0373	6.0373	6.0373	6.0373	6.0373	6.0373
Total level of pollution emissions							
wastewater	100 million tons	237.27	226.96	224.05	236.21	236.08	217.26
smog dust	100 million tons	0.0308	0.0308	0.0308	0.0308	0.0308	0.0308
solid waste	100 million tons	1.1160	1.1127	1.1129	1.1159	1.1165	1.1114
Emission tax	100 million yuan	12.02	10.72	10.35	11.89	12.49	10.73
Household waste tax	100 million yuan	0.00	0.00	7.06	1.65	0.00	0.00
Pollution subsidy	100 million yuan	0.00	0.00	0.00	0.00	0.00	0.00
Pollution compensation	100 million yuan	0.39	0.36	0.35	0.38	0.38	0.34
Utility	unitless	9.33	9.43	9.45	9.34	9.34	9.51

Note:

Base -- the baseyear simulation

S3 -- treat 80 per cent of all industrial wastewater

S4-1 -- tax household wastewater discharge at 0 2 yuan/ton

S4-2 -- tax trash from household at 3.00 yuan/ton.

S5-1 -- the government spends 200 million yuan on wastewater treatment services

S5-2 -- the government spends 400 million yuan on wastewater treatment services

Other control variables in S3-S5 same as those in the base year

the program requires treatment of 80 per cent of all industrial wastewater and 88 per cent of all industrial waste gases by the end of 1998.

The environmental CGE model is a useful tool for assessing the economic impacts of these pollution control objectives. Incorporating waste treatment in the model makes it easy to simulate the effects of requiring treatment for 80 per cent of the wastewater. In 1990, China treated only 64.7 per cent of its industrial wastewater, falling short of the wastewater treatment standard. Only 57.8 per cent of the treated wastewater satisfied the emission standards. In other word, the proportion of wastewater that met the emission standards after treatment, out of the total wastewater treated, was 37.4 per cent in that year.

Assuming that there are no changes in wastewater treatment technology and only 57.8 per cent of the treated wastewater will meet the emission standards, treating 80 per cent of all wastewater means that the percentage of treated wastewater that satisfies emission standards will increase from 37.4 per cent (the base-year value) to 46.2 per cent. Fixing the cleanup rate of wastewater at 46.2 per cent in the model, the economic impacts of treating 80 per cent of all industrial wastewater can then be assessed.

The simulation results, presented in the fourth column (S3) of Table 6.4, demonstrate that total output will decrease by Y 2.7 billion, from Y 4180.7 billion to Y 4178.0 billion, equivalent to a decline of 0.064 per cent. In addition to the decline in production, total income, total investment, and total employment are also negatively affected. The unemployment rate rises from 4.00 per cent to 4.07 per cent because some factories have to be shut down in order to meet environmental requirements.

It is worth mentioning that the simulation results were obtained based on the assumption that no structural and technological changes would occur during the implementation of the wastewater treatment plan. To reflect any structural and technological changes, the relevant portions of the CGE model need to be adjusted. For example, if a reduction in pollution emissions is to be achieved mainly by introducing new and cleaner production equipment, the pollution intensity coefficients must be adjusted correspondingly. If the government's development and investment priorities lean toward the less-polluting industries, the share parameters of investment and consumption by sector of destination should be adjusted.

6.4   Taxing household waste disposal

Household wastes, such as sewage and trash, are becoming another major pollution source in China. Although China has not directly levied a tax on household waste disposal, this tax is a strong possibility in the future.

Because the functions of the household waste disposal tax are already in the environmental CGE model, the model can be used to simulate a household trash tax and a sewage tax. The first simulation assumes a tax of 0.20 yuan per ton on the household sewage discharge, i.e., it taxes household sewage at the same tax rate as industrial wastewater. The second simulation introduces a trash tax of 3 yuan per ton on household trash disposal.

The findings from the scenarios are reported in Table 6.4, in columns 5 and 6 (S4-1 and S4-2). The results show that the government collects Y 0.71 billion and Y 0.17 billion, respectively. Meanwhile, the total household disposable income decreases from Y 873.2 billion to Y 871.7 billion and Y 872.9 billion, respectively. The drop in household disposable income results in a decrease in household consumption demand and thus causes declines in production and employment.

6.5   Government purchase of pollution cleaning services

Besides subsidizing a pollution abatement sector, the government may directly spend money on purchasing pollution cleaning services from that sector, similarly to purchasing consumption goods from a production sector. For example, the municipal government can pay wastewater treatment plants for cleaning municipal sewage.

To examine the possible outcomes of government spending on pollution cleaning services, two scenarios were simulated: (1) the government spends Y 200 million to purchase products from the wastewater treatment sector, i.e., services for treating wastewater; and (2) the government doubles the expenditure to Y 400 million.

The primary results of the simulations are listed in columns 7 and 8 of Table 6.4. Spending Y 200 million on wastewater treatment causes little change in production and pollution control. Doubling the government spending to Y 400 million, however, perceptibly affects the economy and pollution emissions.

Compared with the base-year observation in which no government expenditures on pollution cleaning services are assumed, spending Y 400 million on pollution cleaning services crowds in on government investment and reduces investment demand. The aggregate output of the production sectors is therefore reduced. In addition, total income drops, while the unemployment rate goes up by one-tenth of a percent.

Driven by the increase in government demand for wastewater treatment, the output of the wastewater treatment sector rises in both scenarios. The level of wastewater treatment reaches 6.4 billion tons per year in the high spending scenario, while the growth of wastewater treatment in the low spending scenario is relatively insignificant. The levels of wastewater discharge drop in both cases because of the increase in pollution treatment and the decrease in pollution generation via the decrease in production.

In summary, several possible environmental policy alternatives were simulated in this chapter. The first group of policies under scrutiny were those that increase the tax rate on wastewater discharge. The simulation results show that raising the wastewater discharge fee by 25 per cent, i.e., to 0.25 yuan per ton, has negative effects on production and employment and fails to reduce pollution emissions. Wastewater treatment increases to 73 per cent when the tax rate reaches 0.30 yuan per ton (a 50 per cent increase). This chapter also examined the simulations of pollution abatement subsidies, household waste disposal taxes, and government purchase of pollution cleaning services. To assess the economic impacts of China's five-year environmental protection program, an impact assessment of one of its major objectives, raising wastewater treatment rates to 80 per cent, was also conducted.

Notes

1   See the World Bank (1992).
2   See also Florig et al. (1995).
3   See Pearce and Turner (1990).
4   The model assumes that capital is utilized fully in production processes, i.e., no idle equipment is allowed. Therefore, when an economy has a recession, the most capital-intensive sector in the economy, the energy sector in the seven-sector Chinese economy, for example, will tend to attract more capital and increase its production. This assumption can be further adjusted if necessary.

5   In 1990, the Chinese government collected 950 million yuan in wastewater emission taxes and invested 450 million yuan in controlling wastewater sources. The amounts of the subsidies were somewhat arbitrarily assigned in the experiments, but are feasible given the government's pollution emission tax revenue.

6   See *People's Daily* (overseas edition), February 3, 1994.

7 Summary, conclusions and suggestions for further study

This chapter is devoted to a summary of the major findings of this book. Section 7.1 summarizes the dissertation. Section 7.2 offers conclusions concerning the methodological contributions, and section 7.3 offers conclusions about the findings of the policy simulations. Section 7.4 provides suggestions for further study.

7.1   Summary of the book

The objectives of this research were twofold. The first was to develop an improved environmental CGE model. The second was to apply the model to China for simulations of Chinese environmental policies.

After the brief introductory chapter, Chapter 2 reviewed the literature on CGE modeling. The chapter suggested that the CGE approach, defined by its endogenous determination of prices, non-linearity, and inclusion of supply constraints, is capable of more accurately simulating the general equilibrium effects of a policy change or an external shock than other types of economic modeling techniques, such as the I/O technique.

Since the late 1970s, CGE models have been widely used for policy analyses in both developed and developing countries. The application of CGE models to environmental policy analysis emerged in the late 1980s. Although about 20 CGE models have been applied to environmental policy issues, the use of CGE models for environmental policy analysis is still in its early stages. The four apparent gaps in the application of environmental CGE models are as follows. First, pollution-related activities and the interactions between production and pollution are partially or weakly defined in many of the environmental CGE models, which undermines the reliability and comprehensiveness of CGE applications to environmental policy simu-

111

lations. Second, most environmental CGE models lack an integrated economic and environmental accounting framework for their parameter specification. Many are parameterized on partial or stylized environmental accounting matrices. Third, most, if not all, environmental CGE models have been built for developed countries. The application of CGE models for environmental policy analysis in developing countries lags far behind the need for such application. Finally, although a few CGE models of the Chinese economy have been presented since the late 1980s, none of them has been designed for environmental policy analysis.

In an effort to overcome the weaknesses of the existing environmental CGE models, an improved environmental CGE model was developed in chapter 3. This model integrates various pollution-related activities in a standard CGE modeling framework. The economic part of the model is similar to that of a standard CGE model for developing countries. However, the model is unique in the way it combines pollution-related activities with economic activities within a CGE framework. The major environmental components incorporated in this environmental CGE model are: (1) pollution abatement activities and pollution abatement costs to (or payments by) production sectors; (2) pollution taxes, such as production pollution emission taxes and household waste disposal taxes; (3) pollution abatement subsidies; (4) environmental compensation; (5) separately specified environmental investment and environmental investment demands; and (6) various pollution indicators, including pollution cleanup ratios and the levels of pollution abatement and emissions.

In an economy that taxes the pollution emissions of production sectors, polluting production sectors must pay for their pollution discharges. However, instead of paying the full pollution emission taxes, pollution sectors may choose to pay pollution abatement sectors to reduce their pollution emissions. Hence, the model explicitly specifies these two pollution-related costs of production activities: pollution emission taxes and pollution abatement costs. The pollution emission tax collected on the pollution discharge of a production sector is determined jointly by the sector's output, pollution intensities, pollution cleanup rates, and pollution emission tax rates. The pollution abatement cost of a sector is a function of its output, pollution intensities, proportion of pollution abatement to total pollution generation, and the prices of pollution cleaning services.

Similarly to the production sectors, the production of a pollution abatement sector is determined by a Cobb-Douglas production function with the inputs of two primary factors: labor and capital. Pollution abatement sectors sell their services, i.e., pollution cleanup, to polluting sectors. The

112

prices of pollution cleaning services are determined by the market via demand and supply.

Pollution abatement subsidies, household waste disposal taxes, and environmental compensation are also incorporated in the model. In one way or another, they affect income distribution, consumption demand, savings, and investments. In the model, environmental investments in pollution control activities are accounted for separately and are mapped from the sectors of destination to the sectors of origin.

Although the possible negative impacts of pollution emissions and environmental quality deterioration on productivity were previously discussed, they were not specified in the model because most developing countries do not have sufficient data or information in this respect. In addition, the applied model focuses on measuring the economic losses and benefits of policy changes. It lacks the ability to represent the non-monetary benefits or losses from pollution emission reductions.

The parameter estimation of a model is as important as the model specification itself. Chapter 4 examined two widely used approaches in parameter estimation of CGE models: the econometric approach and the calibration approach. Although the econometric approach is statistically more sound, the calibration approach was adopted in this study because of its limited data requirements and the ease of parameter computation.

To facilitate the calibration of the environmental CGE model, an environmentally extended social accounting matrix (ESAM) was developed in chapter 4. In the ESAM, pollution abatement activities are distinguished from production activities in the activity accounts, and the pollutants abated are treated as special goods in the commodity accounts. Pollution emission taxes, pollution abatement costs, pollution abatement subsidies, and environmental investment are also accounted for separately. The ESAM provides an integrated, consistent equilibrium data set that can be easily used for the calibration of the environmental CGE model developed in this study.

Chapters 5 and 6 applied the environmental CGE model to China for environmental policy analyses. The environmental CGE model of China has seven production sectors (agriculture, mining, light industry, energy, heavy industry, construction, and services) and three pollution abatement sectors (wastewater, smog dust and solid waste). Unlike other CGE models of the Chinese economy, this model does not explicitly attempt to separate the prices and goods under market and under plans. Cobb-Douglas production functions are employed in both the production and pollution abatement sectors. The model assumes that the economy-wide average wage rate is

113

rigid and that aggregate labor and capital supplies are exogenously determined. Other exogenous variables include the foreign exchange rate, government spending on consumption goods, government subsidies, and debt.

Based on the conceptual framework of the ESAM developed in section 4.3 of chapter 4, an ESAM was constructed. The ESAM contains the production and pollution abatement sectors included in the environmental CGE model of China and was mainly used in the research as an integrated equilibrium data set for calibrating the environmental CGE model.

To test the robustness of the model's solutions to changes in parameters, sensitivity analyses were conducted. The conditional systematic sensitivity analyses (CSSA) approach was adopted, given its parsimony in computation and its lack of a need for a large amount of prior information. Unlike the sensitivity analyses of many other CGE models, which emphasize the effects of substitution elasticities on trade, the attention of the sensitivity analyses for this model was focused on the stability of the model's solutions to changes in the pollution-related parameters. The wastewater intensity coefficients of light industry and heavy industry were disturbed because those coefficients are important and likely to be subject to measurement errors. The sensitivity analysis results indicate that the model is robust regarding minor errors in pollution intensities.

The Chinese government began to take action against industrial pollution in the 1970s. A series of environmental policies, programs, and regulations have been put in place since then. The major environmental policies or methods currently implemented include an environmental impact assessment system, an industrial pollution effluent fee system, an environmental protection fund, and a pollution emission permit system. In 1994, the Chinese government launched a five-year environmental protection program. The major goals of the program are to treat 80 per cent of all industrial wastewater and 88 per cent of all industrial waste gases by the end of 1998.

Environmental policy analyses, using the proposed environmental CGE model of China, were presented in chapter 6. The analyses focused first on the Chinese pollution effluent fee system. The effluent fees in China have been criticized as being too low to give polluters an incentive to reduce their pollution emissions. The scenarios of incrementally raising the tax rate on wastewater emissions were tested. The model was also used to evaluate the economic impacts of treating 80 per cent of industrial wastewater, as required by in China's newly launched five-year environmental program. Other types of environmental policy simulations conducted in this chapter were subsidizing pollution abatement sectors, taxing household waste disposal, and increasing government spending on the purchase of pollution cleaning services.

7.2   Conclusions of methodological contributions

This research contributes to the literature on the methodology of CGE modeling for environmental policy analysis, environmental accounting, and Chinese environmental policy simulation. The three contributions are described as follows.

The first contribution of the research is in its development of an environmental CGE model. As the literature review indicated, the model is one of the few that have integrated many environmental policy variables, pollution control activities, and pollution-production interactions in a conventional CGE model. The ways that the model defines pollution abatement activities, specifies pollution-related costs in production sectors, and determines optimal production levels considering pollution control requirements are unique and implementable, compared with other environmental CGE models. The application of the model to China shows that the model has the advantage of simulating various environmental policies in the real world.

The second contribution of the research -- the presentation of an environmentally extended social accounting matrix (ESAM) framework -- makes the numerical specification of the model easy to implement. The ESAM framework contributes to the field of environmental accounting by its approach of taking into account environmental data in a conventional SAM framework. Among the variety of environmental data accounted for separately in the ESAM, pollution abatement activities are separated from production activities in the activity account, and pollution cleaning services are listed as special goods in the commodity account. The ESAM successfully provides an integrated, consistent equilibrium database for the initialization and parameter specification of the environmental CGE model.

The third contribution of the research is the application of environmental CGE model to China for environmental policy analysis. This model appears to be the first CGE model designed for Chinese environmental policy analysis. Because China is the world's largest developing country and one of the most crucial nations impacting the global environment, the study of Chinese environmental policy analysis is very important. The policy-related findings from the case study of China thus are important and can be used by other developing countries for reference.

7.3   Conclusions of policy-related findings

The following four groups of environmental policy alternatives were simulated: (1) raising the tax rate on wastewater discharge; (2) subsidizing the wastewater treatment sector; (3) taxing household sewage and trash; and (4) the increasing government's purchase of wastewater cleaning services. In addition, the economic impacts of treating 80 per cent of industrial wastewater, one of the major goals of China's five-year environmental protection program, were assessed.

Table 7.1
Comparison of results of environmental policy simulations
(++: large increase, +: small increase, n.c.: no change,
-: small decrease, --: large decrease)

	S1-1	S1-2	S2	S3	S4	S5	Range of % change
Total output	-	--	-	-	-	-	-0.011% to -0.246%
Unemploy. rate	+	++	++	+	++	++	0.50% to 5.75%
Price index	+	++	n.c.	+	+	+	+0.000% to 0.030%
Total income	-	-	-	-	-	-	-0.021% to -0.225%
Gov't revenue	+	-	-	-	+	-	-0.272% to +0.064%
Net foreign reserve	-	--	-	-	-	+	0.010% to -0.602%
Investment	n.c.	-	-	-	-	-	-0.000% to -0.303%
Real GDP	-	--	--	-	-	-	-0.012% to -0.260%
Wastewater abated	n.c.	++	++	+	+	+	0 to 73.06%
Wastewater emitted	n.c.	--	--	-	-	-	0 to -14.10%
Emission tax	+	-	-	-	-	-	-24.21% to +20.21%
Utility	-	+	+	+	+	+	-0.107% to +2.89%

Note:

List of policy scenarios:

S1-1 -- raise the tax rate on industrial wastewater by 25%.

S1-2 -- raise the tax rate on industrial wastewater by 50%.

S2 -- subsidize the wastewater treatment sector by 400 million yuan.

S3 -- treat 80% of industrial wastewater.

S4 -- tax household wastewater discharge by 0.2 yuan/ton.

S5 -- government spends 400 million yuan to buy wastewater treatment services.

The policy simulations from the environmental CGE model provide much information about the economic and environmental impacts of the policy alternatives and programs. Table 7.1 qualitatively summarizes the key results of the simulations.

Generally speaking, the results indicate that the pollution control policies have negative effects on economic growth. Decreases in production, employment, income, and investment are observed in all of the policy simulations. The effectiveness of the policies on wastewater treatment varies in magnitude. Raising the tax rate on wastewater discharge by 25 per cent (S1-1) is still too low to create an incentive for polluters to reduce their wastewater discharges. But when the tax rate is increased by 50 per cent (S1-2), the demand for wastewater treatment increases by 70 per cent. The pollution reduction, however, has to be traded off with a drop in production output if no structural or technological changes occur in the economy. The production output drops by 0.22 per cent. The results of the policy simulations show that the policy alternatives of subsidizing the wastewater treatment sector (S2) and increasing government spending on the purchase of wastewater treatment (S5) are also effective in reducing wastewater discharge.

The detailed sectoral changes in outputs are also given in the simulation results. The magnitudes of sectoral output changes regarding each pollution control policy vary from one sector to another, and both polluting sectors and non-polluting sectors are affected by the pollution control policies. After examining the sectoral changes in outputs of pollution abatement subsidies, it can be concluded that the pollution abatement subsidy is unfavorable because it actually protects pollution-intensive sectors from being punished for their pollution generation.

7.4   Suggestions for further study

Further study of this topic can take at least two directions: improving the model and applying the model to a broader spectrum of policy analyses.

Improving the model

The model could be refined in several respects. First, the demand by a production sector for pollution abatement services is currently specified in a simplified way. It uses average pollution cleanup rates and assumes that the unit costs for pollution abatement are independent of the cleanup rates. With more exploration into the economics of pollution abatement, the demand function could be more accurately defined, and the cleanup rates

117

could be made sectorally specific. These modifications would bring the model closer to the real-world case.

Second, the pollution abatement sectors are assumed, like any other production sector, to seek their own optimal production levels, and the prices of pollution abatement services are assumed to be determined by the market. These assumptions might not be true for a pollution abatement sector or facility that is affiliated with a production sector and does not attempt to make a profit on its own. In such a case, the price of the pollution abatement service needs to be fixed, normally, at the average unit cost of pollution abatement.

Third, as mentioned earlier, the ESAM used for calibrating the model is highly aggregated and was estimated based on some rigid assumptions. The ESAM could be further improved as more disaggregated and accurate data become available. Also, the simplified capital composition matrix, which is uniform across sectors using the share of aggregate investment by sectors, could be improved and made sectorally specific as capital composition data by sectors become available.

In addition to the modifications on the pollution side, there is room for improving the model with respect to its production functions and its static nature. The more sophisticated nested CES production function could replace the simple Cobb-Douglas production function in the model. The static model could also be upgraded to an inter-temporal or dynamic model by carefully defining the relationship between investments and fixed assets.

Additional policy analyses

Applications of the environmental CGE model for policy analysis are not limited to the few policies presented in the previous chapter. The model provides decision makers and policy analysts with an opportunity to conduct policy analysis from various policy perspectives. Some opportunities for other types of policy analysis are noted below.

As noted earlier, the current pollution levy system in China is ineffective in reducing pollution emissions. It has been observed that the ineffectiveness is caused not only by the low effluent fees but also by the weak legal enforcement of pollution emission taxation. Therefore, pollution emissions could be reduced by strengthening enforcement of pollution emission tax collection. The pollution emission tax equation includes an implementation adjustment factor to capture the difference between the planned pollution emission taxes and the pollution emission taxes that are actually collected. By increasing the implementation factor, the outcomes of enhancing the legal enforcement of pollution emission taxes on the economy and on pollution control could be examined.

Upgrading equipment and production technology is a very effective approach in reducing pollution generation and emissions. Like other countries, China has paid great attention to importing advanced and less-polluting technology to increase productivity and reduce pollution intensities.[1] The economic and environmental impacts of technological improvement could be assessed by changing the relevant technical coefficients, such as the input-output coefficients and the pollution intensity coefficients, in the model.

The incorporation in the model of the share parameter (βk_{ia}), representing environmental investment by the pollution abatement sectors, allows experimentation with changes in environmental investment allocation. The results from such experiments would be useful in guiding a country's investment policy. However, to conduct such experiments, the current model needs to be modified in two respects. First, the model's static nature prevents the inter-temporal effects of changes in investment allocation on production from being studied. In order to capture those effects, the static model needs to be converted into an inter-temporal one that explicitly specifies the relationships between investments and fixed assets. Second, because data representing the composition of the capital spending of each sector on investment goods were not available, the model assumes that the shares of the investment of each sector by sectors are the same as the shares of the aggregate investment by sectors. In order to experiment with changes in environmental investment allocations, the capital composition coefficients have to be specified by sectors.

Environmental compensation by polluters to the agents who suffer from the pollution are included in the model. Environmental compensation is measured using the fixed ratio of the amount of pollution compensation to total pollution emissions. With these environmental compensation components in the model, the scenarios of adjusting environmental compensation ratios or changing the flow of the compensation from its origin to a different destination could be examined.

The government and households may adjust their spending priorities according to the polluting nature of the products, e.g., by shifting their spending from polluting products to clean products. Adjusting the share parameters of government expenditure or total private consumption by sectors would allow experimentation with possible changes in government spending priorities or household consumption preferences.

119

Although the application of the model focused on environmental policy analyses, the model is also useful for analyzing the environmental impacts of an economic policy. For example, the Chinese government is planning to further increase coal production and to develop a family car industry. With an appropriate sector classification, the model could be used to assess the impacts of these policies on China's environment. Finally, by disaggregating the single household category into different economic classes such as rural, urban poor, and urban rich, the model could be used to assess the social impact of environmental policies. For example, the impact of household waste disposal taxes on income distribution among economic classes could be assessed.

Notes

1   Funded by the World Bank, the National EPA of China is currently implementing a project that aims at reducing pollution emission intensities through promoting cleaner production technologies.

Appendix
The GAMS program listing of the environmental CGE model for China

AN ENVIRONMENTAL CGE MODEL FOR CHINA, JIAN XIE, CORNELL UNIVERSITY

THIS GENERAL EQUILIBRIUM MODEL IS DESIGNED AS A TOOL
FOR CHINESE ENVIRONMENTAL POLICY ANALYSIS   IT IS CALIBRATED
TO THE 1990 7-SECTOR ENVIRONMENTALLY EXTENDED SAM OF CHINA

THE ECONOMIC PART OF THE MODEL FOLLOWS CLOSELY THE CAMEROON MODELS
DEVELOPED BY CONDON, DAHL, AND DEVARAJAN(1986), AND DEVARAJAN, LEWIS, AND
ROBINSON(1991). IN ORDER TO CAPTURE THE IMPACTS OF ENVIRONMENTAL
REQUIREMENTS OR REGULATIONS ON AN ECONOMY, POLLUTION CONTROL ACTIVITIES
INCLUDING POLLUTION TAXES, SUBSIDIES, AND ABATEMENT ACTIVITIES ARE
INCORPORATED INTO THE MODEL. THE MODEL ALSO INCLUDES HOUSEHOLD WASTE
DISPOSAL TAXES AND ENVIRONMENTAL COMPENSATION. IN ADDITION,
ENVIRONMENTAL INVESTMENT DEMANDS ARE SEPARATELY ACCOUNTED FOR
IN THE MODEL.

THE MODEL IS ORIGINALLY DESIGNED FOR A CITY   BUT IT IS EASY TO APPLY
THIS MODEL AT THE NATIONAL LEVEL BY SETTING THE TRADES, SAVINGS AND
GOVERNMENT REVENUE TRANSFER BETWEEN THE CITY AND THE REST OF THE
COUNTRY EQUAL TO ZERO

CURRENCY EQUIVALENT
 CURRENCY UNIT: YUAN (Y)
 OFFICIAL EXCHANGE RATE IN 1990: 4 78 YUAN PER U S DOLLAR
30
31 *##### SET DECLARATION #####
32
33 SET I SECTORS
34   / AG AGRICULTURE
35   MN MINING
36   LG LIGHT INDUSTRY
37   EN ENERGY INDUSTRY
38   HE HEAVY INDUSTRY
39   CS CONSTRUCTION
40   SV SERVICES
41   WA WASTE WATER TREATMENT SECOTR
42   SD SMOG DUST ABATEMENT SECTOR
43   SW SOLID WASTE TREATMENT SECTOR /
44
45   IA(I) POLLUTION ABATEMENT SECTORS
46   / WA, SD, SW /
47

```
48   IP(I) PRODUCTION SECTORS
49   IE(I) EXPORT SECTORS
50   IM(I) IMPORT SECTOR
51   IEN(I) NON EXPORT SECTOR
52   IMN(I) NON IMPORT SECTOR
53   IC(I)  SECTORS PROVIDING GOODS FOR FINAL CONSUMPTION
54
55   ALIAS (IP, JP)
56   ALIAS (IA, G)
57   ALIAS (I, J);
58   IP(I)= NOT IA(I);
59
60  *##### PARAMETER DECLARATION #####
61
62  PARAMETERS
63   WLDIST(I)  SECTOR SPECIFIC PARAMETER FOR WAGE
64   WKDIST(I)  SECTOR SPECIFIC PARAMETER FOR CAPITAL RETURN
65   DELTA(I)  ARMINGTON FUNCTION SHARE PARAMETER
66   AC(I)  ARMINGTON FUNCTION SHIFT PARAMETER
67   RHOC(I)  ARMINGTON FUNCTION EXPONENT
68   RHOT(I)  CET FUNCTION EXPONENT
69   AT(I)   CET FUNCTION SHIFT PARAMETER
70   GAMMA(I)  CET FUNCTION SHARE PARAMETER
71   AD(I)   PRODUCTION FUNCTION SHIFT PARAMETER
72   QD(I)   DUMMY VARIABLE FOR COMPUTING AD(I)
73   CLES(I)  PRIVATE CONSUMPTION SHARES
74   GLES(I)  GOVERNMENT CONSUMPTION SHARES
75   PLES(G)  EXPONENT OF POLLUTION ABATEMENT IN UTILTIY FUNCTION
76   DEPR(I) DEPRECIATION RATES
77   DSTR(I) RATIO OF INVENTORY INVESTMENT TO GROSS OUTPUT
78   KIO(I)  SHARES OF INVESTMENT BY SECTOR OF DESTINATION
79   TE(I)  EXPORT DUTY RATES
80   ITAX(I) INDIRECT TAX RATES
81   ALPHL(I)  LABOR SHARE PARAMETER IN PRODUCTION FUNCTION
82   AEC(I)   RATIO OF EXPORT TO ROC TO OUTPUT
83   AMC(I)   RATIO OF IMPORT FROM ROC TO OUTPUT
84   SUMBBSH(I)  COLUMN SUM OF CAPITAL COMPOSITION MATRIX BB
85   TD(G,I)  ADJUSTED POLLUTION COEFFICIENT MATRIX (0 REPLACED BY 1)
86   ADJ(IA,I)  ADJUSTMENT FACTOR FOR ABATEMENT PAYMENT
87   IMPL0(IA,I) ADJUSTMENT FACTOR FOR POLLUTION EMISSION TAXES
88
89  *DUMMIES TO HOLD INITIAL DATA FROM 1990 ESAM OF CHINA
90
91   M0(I)   VOLUME OF IMPORTS ('90 Y 100 MILLION)
92   E0(I)   VOLUME OF EXPORTS ('90 Y 100 MILLION)
93   MC0(I)  VOLUME OF IMPORT FROM ROC ('90 Y 100 MILLION)
94   EC0(I)  VOLUME OF EXPORT TO ROC ('90 Y 100 MILLION)
95   XD0(I)  VOLUME OF DOMESTIC OUTPUT BY SECTOR ('90 Y 100 MILLION)
96   TXD  TOTAL DOMESTIC OUTPUT ('90 Y 100 MILLION)
97   TXD0  TOTAL DOMESTIC OUTPUT IN THE BASE YEAR ('90 Y 100 MILLION)
98   INT0(I) VOLUME OF INTERMEDIATE INPUT DEMANDS ('90 Y 100 MILLION)
99   ID0(I)  VOLUME OF INVESTMENT BY SECTOR OF ORIGIN ('90 Y 100 MILLION)
100  KIOE0(IA) SHARE OF ENV. INVESTMENT BY POLLUTION ABATEMENT SECTORS (UNITLESS)
101  IDE0(I)  VOLUME OF ENV. INVESTMENT BY SECTOR OF ORIGIN ('90 Y 100 MILLION)
102  DST0(I)  VOLUME OF INVENTORY INVESTMENT BY SECTOR ('90 Y 100 MILLION)
103  XXD0(I)  VOLUME OF DOMESTIC SALES BY SECTOR  ('90 Y 100 MILLION)
104  CD0(I)   VOLUME OF HOUSEHOLD CONSUMPTION BY SECTOR ('90 Y 100 MILLION)
105  TCD  TOTAL HOUSEHOLD CONSUMPTION ('90 Y 100 MILLION)
106  TCD0  TOTAL HOUSEHOLD CONSUMPTION IN THE BASE YEAR ('90 Y 100 MILLION)
107  GD0(I)  VOLUME OF GOVERNMENT CONSUMPTION BY SECTOR ('90 Y 100 MILLION)
108  CDTOT0  TOTAL PRIVATE CONSUMPTION ('90 Y 100 MILLION)
109  GDTOT0  TOTAL GOVERNMENT CONSUMPTION  ('90 Y 100 MILLION)
110  X0(I)  VOLUME OF COMPOSITE GOOD SUPPLY ('90 Y 100 MILLION)
```

```
111  PWE0(I) WORLD MARKET PRICE OF EXPORTS (UNITY)
112  PWM0(I) WORLD MARKET PRICE OF IMPORTS (UNITY)
113  PD0(I) DOMESTIC GOOD PRICE (UNITY)
114  PE0(I) DOMESTIC PRICE OF EXPORTS (UNITY)
115  PM0(I) DOMESTIC PRICE OF IMPORTS (UNITY)
116  PX0(I) PRICE OF OUTPUT (UNITY)
117  P0(I)  PRICE OF COMPOSITE GOODS (UNITY)
118  PVA0(I) VALUE ADDED PRICE BY SECTOR (UNITY)
119  PK0(I) PRICE OF CAPITAL INVESTMENT (UNITY)
120  PINDEX0 PRICE INDEX IN THE BASE YEAR  (UNITY)
121  SUB0(I) GOVERNMENT SUBSIDY TO ENTERPRISES ('90 Y 100 MILLION)
122  L0(I)  LABOR DEMAND BY SECTOR IN BASE YEAR (MILLION PERSONS)
123  XLLB(I) DUMMY VARIABLE (L MATRIX WITH NO ZEROS)
124  LD   TOTAL EMPLOYMENT (MILLION PERSONS)
125  LS0  TOTAL LABOR SUPPLY (MILLION PERSONS)
126  RUNEMP0 UNEMPLOYMENT RATE (UNITLESS)
127  WL0  AVERAGE WAGE RATE ('90 100 MILLION YUAN PER MILLION WORKER)
128  K0(I)  VOLUME OF CAPITAL STOCKS BY SECTOR  ('90 Y 100 MILLION)
129  KS0  TOTAL CAPITAL STOCK ('90 Y 100 MILLION)
130  WK0  AVERAGE CAPITAL RETURN RATE (UNITLESS)
131  Y0  TOTAL VALUE-ADDED ('90 Y 100 MILLION)
132  LBINC0  HOUSEHOLD LABOR INCOME ('90 Y 100 MILLION)
133  YC0  ENTERPRISE CAPITAL INCOME ('90 Y 100 MILLION)
134  TARIFF0  TARIFF REVENUE ('90 Y 100 MILLION)
135  INDTAX0  INDIRECT TAX REVENUE  ('90 Y 100 MILLION)
136  CSUB0  TOTAL GOVERNMENT SUBSIDIES TO ENTERPRISES ('90 Y 100 MILLION)
137  EXPSUB0  EXPORT SUBSIDY  ('90 Y 100 MILLION)
138  TM0(I)  TARIFF RATES (UNITLESS)
139  TPE0(G)  POLLUTION EMISSION TAX ('90 YUAN PER TON)
140  TPD0(G)  HOUSEHOLD POLLUTION DISPOSAL TAX ('90 YUAN PER TON)
141  ETAX0  TOTAL POLLUTION EMISSION TAX REVENUE ('90 Y 100 MILLION)
142  DSUB0  GOVERNMENT SUBSIDY TO POLLUTION CONTROL ('90 Y 100 MILLION)
143  PA0(IA)  PRICE OF POLLUTANT ABATED ('90 YUAN PER TON)
144  DA0(IA)  POLLUTANT ABATED BY POLLUTANT AND BY SECTOR (100 MILLION TONS)
145  TDA0(IA)  TOTAL POLLUTANT ABATED BY POLLUTANT (100 MILLION TONS)
146  DG0(G)  LEVEL OF POLLUTION GENERATION BY POLLUTANTS (100 MILLION TONS)
147  DE0(G)  TOTAL AMOUNT OF POLLUTION DISCHARGED (100 MILLION TONS)
148  REC0(G)  COEFFICIENT FOR POLLUTION COMPENSATION ('90 YUAN PER TON)
149  DCOMP0(G)  ENVIRONMENTAL COMPENSATION BY POLLUTANTS ('90 Y 100 MILLION)
150  DCOMPEN0  TOTAL ENVIRONMENTAL COMPENSATION ('90 Y 100 MILLION)
151  DTAX0  TOTAL HOUSEHOLD WASTE DISPOSAL TAX ('90 Y 100 MILLION)
152  CL0(G)  CLEANUP RATE BY POLLUTANT AND BY SECTOR (UNITLESS)
153  S(G)  % OF POLLUTION GENERATION SUBJECT TO EMISSION TAXES (UNITLESS)
154  GDPVA0 NOMINAL GDP IN THE BASE YEAR ('90 Y 100 MILLION)
155  RGDP0 REAL GDP IN THE BASE YEAR ('90 Y 100 MILLION)
156  UTILITY0  INITIAL VALUE OF UTILITY ('90 Y 100 MILLION)
157  ,
158
159  *##### BASE DATA AND PARAMETER ASSIGNMENT #####
160
161  SCALARS
162  ER0  REAL EXCHANGE RATE IN 1990 (YUAN PER U S DALLOR) /4 780/
163  RUNEMP0 UNEMPLOYMENT RATE IN 1990 (UNITLESS) /0 0400/
164  GR0  GOVERNMENT REVENUE ('90 Y 100 MILLION) /3701 1/
165  TYC0  TAX RATE ON CORPORATE REVENUE ('90 Y 100 MILLION)  /0 42275/
166  TYH0  TAX RATE ON HOUSEHOLD INCOME ('90 Y 100 MILLION) /0 0000/
167  MPS0  MARGINAL PROPENSITY TO SAVE (UNITLESS) /0 14971/
168  HSUB0  HOUSEHOLD SUBSIDY ('90 Y 100 MILLION) /435 8/
169  FDEBT0  GOVERNMENT BORROWING FROM ABROAD ('90 Y 100 MILLION) /110 00/
170  DDEBT0  GOVERNMENT DOMESTIC BORROWING ('90 Y 100 MILLION) /75 1/
171  DEFICIT0  DEFICIT ('90 Y 100 MILLION) /139 6/
172  GADJ0  GOVERNMENT INCOME ADJUSTMENT ('90 Y 100 MILLION) /0/
173  REMIT0  HOUSEHOLD INCOME FROM ABROAD ('90 Y 100 MILLION) /9 30/
```

174 HHSAV0 HOUSEHOLD SAVING ('90 Y 100 MILLION) /1460 79/
175 CSAV0 SAVING BY COMPANY ('90 Y 100 MILLION) /2391 73/
176 GSAV0 GOVERNMENT SAVING ('90 Y 100 MILLION) /899 55/
177 ROCSAV0 SAVING FROM THE REST OF THE COUNTRY /0/
178 SAVING0 TOTAL SAVING ('90 Y 100 MILLION) /6574 22/
179 INVROC0 INVESTMENT FROM THE REST OF THE COUNTRY ('90 Y 100 MILLION) /0/
180 BSPLUS0 SURPLUS IN BALANCE OF PAYMENT ('90 Y 100 MILLION) /683.32/
181 EINV0 ENVIRONMENTAL INVESTMENT ('90 Y 100 MILLION) /34 13/
182 ,
184
185 TABLE IO(I,J) INPUT-OUTPUT COEFFICIENTS (UNITLESS)
186   AG   MN   LG   EN   HE
187 AG 0.1784735 0.0337990 0 2713733 0 0006160 0 0271172
188 MN 0.0006658 0.0342231 0.0054174 0 3276278 0 0437245
189 LG 0.0432900 0.0364056 0.2888042 0 0145815 0 0583433
190 EN 0 0084465 0 0690878 0 0100521 0 0567137 0 0540247
191 HE 0 0751309 0 2967500 0 0828244 0 0993394 0 4577282
192 CS 0 0000000 0.0000000 0 0000000 0.0000000 0.0000000
193 SV 0.0367104 0.0730589 0 0916643 0 1065816 0 0807539
194 + CS   SV   WA   SD   SW
195 AG 0.0053474 0.0223311 0 0000000 0 0000000 0 0000000
196 MN 0.0534412 0 0084549 0 0147104 0 0075003 0 0006888
197 LG 0.0323797 0 0780202 0.0326527 0.0395227 0 0384309
198 EN 0.0203398 0.0379747 0 4295050 0 5229576 0 4453818
199 HE 0.5330998 0.1320738 0.1224298 0 1170262 0 0432885
200 CS 0 0000000 0 0000000 0 0000000 0.0000000 0 0000000
201 SV 0.0705660 0 1484825 0 0222351 0 0095214 0 1323433
202 ,
203
204 TABLE BB(I,J) CAPITAL COMPOSITION MATRIX (UNITLESS)
205
206   AG   MN   LG   EN   HE
207 AG 0 0276572 0.0276572 0 0276572 0 0276572 0.0276572
208 MN 0.0000000 0   0   0   0
209 LG 0 0029557 0.00295566 0.00295566 0 00295566 0.00295566
210 EN 0.0000000 0   0   0   0
211 HE 0.3076071 0.30760711 0 30760711 0 30760711 0 30760711
212 CS 0 6435487 0.64354868 0.64354868 0 64354868 0 64354868
213 SV 0.0182314 0 01823136 0.01823136 0 01823136 0.01823136
214 WA 0   0   0   0   0
215 SD 0   0   0   0   0
216 SW 0   0   0   0   0
217 + CS   SV   WA   SD   SW
218 AG 0.0276572 0.0276572 0.000 0 000 0 000
219 MN 0.0000000 0 0000000 0   0 000 0.000
220 LG 0.0029557 0.0029557 0 043 0.043 0.043
221 EN 0 0000000 0.0000000 0   0.000 0.000
222 HE 0 3076071 0.3076071 0.957 0 957 0 957
223 CS 0.6435487 0 6435487 0 000 0 000 0 000
224 SV 0.0182314 0.0182314 0.000 0.000 0 000
225 WA 0   0   0   0   0
226 SD 0   0   0 | 0   0
227 SW 0   0   0   0   0
228 ;
229
230 *REDUCE ROUND ERROR
231 SUMBBSH(I)=SUM(J, BB(J,I));
232 BB(I,J)=BB(I,J)/SUMBBSH(J);
233
234 TABLE ZZ(*,I) MISCELLANEOUS PARAMETERS AND INITIAL DATA
235
236   AG   MN   LG   EN   HE
237 XD0   7659.9608 1366 9045 8074.8536 1460 9627 12615 6150

```
238 EC0   0 00     0 00     0 00     0 00     0 00
239 E0    384.00   373 00   857 00   52 00    1302 00
240 MC0   0.00     0 00     0 00     0 00     0 00
241 M0    214 00   443 00   274 00   0 00     1620 00
242 LBINC 4352 75040 402 34931 774 62816 105 97675 1425 26339
243 KINC  470 01040 146 69360 585 35955 185 19375 1243 24855
244 L0    341.7700  13.1300  28 5206  3 6801   51 6437
245 K0    2480.00000 1546 2844 3288 7871 1465 4128 7128 27867
246 DEPR  124 00000 138 45999 229 27167 124 88969 531 15556
247 RHOC  2.00     0.75     0 75     0 50     0 50
248 RHOT  2 00     1 10     1 10     0 50     0 90
249 ETA   1 0000   1 0000   1 0000   1 0000   1 0000
250 PD0   1 0000   1 0000   1 0000   1 0000   1 0000
251 TE0   0 0      0 0      0 0      0 0      0 0
252 TRF0  10 00    10.00    83 00    0 00     56 00
253 ITAX  88 0     66 72    554 12   180 43   572 66
254 SUB0  0 00     134 00   134.00   26 00    285 00
255 CD0   3058 95  87 52    2678 92  100 38   937 59
256 GD0   15.75    0 00     173 30   0 00     95 16
257 DST0  161.05   6 18     545 16   -59 42   268 21
258 ID0   131 000  0.000    14 00    0 000    1457 00
259 KIO   0 03042  0.12353  0 08234  0 17435  0 25128
260 IDE0  0 00     0 00     1 47     0 00     32 66
261 +     CS       SV       WA       SD       SW
262 XD0   3048 2097 7581 3666 18 3284 5 1853  6 2835
263 EC0   0 00     0 00     0 00     0 00     0 00
264 E0    0.00     147 00   0 00     0 00     0 00
265 MC0   0.00     0 00     0 00     0 00     0 00
266 M0    0 00     0 00     0 00     0.00     0 00
267 LBINC 620 18335 2137 06100 2 90947 0 42206 1 06412
268 KINC  146 02635 1367 78560 0 00000 0 00000 0 00000
269 L0    24 6100  104.0500  0 1054  0 0153   0 0386
270 K0    1280.0000 13047.7193 53 6964 15 3538 14 28566
271 DEPR  64.00000 743 72000 4 02723 1 15153 1 07142
272 RHOC  0.50     0 50     0 50     0 50     0 50
273 RHOT  0 50     0 50     1 00     1 00     1 00
274 ETA   1 0000   1 0000   1 0000   1 0000   1 0000
275 PD0   1.0000   1 0000   1 0000   1 0000   1 0000
276 TE0   0 0      0 0      0 0      0 0      0 0
277 TRF0  0 00     0.0000   0 0000   0 0000   0 0000
278 ITAX  38 00    93.00    0 0000   0 0000   0 0000
279 SUB0  0.00     0 00     0 00     0 00     0 00
280 CD0   0 00     1869 04  0 00     0 00     0 00
281 GD0   0 00     1642 14  0 00     0 00     0 00
282 DST0  0 00     199 03   0 00     0 00     0 00
283 ID0   3048 21  86 354   0 000    0 000    0 000
284 KIO   0.00714  0 33094  0        0        0
285 IDE0  0 00     0 00     0 00     0 00     0 00
286 ,
287
288 TABLE DD(*,G)  INITIAL VALUES RELATED TO POLLUTION CONTROL
289      WA    SD    SW
290 TPE0 0.20  178 0  3 00
291 TPD0 0 00  0.0   0 0
292 KIOE0 0.6335 0.2168 0 1497
293 REC0 0 0024 2 3104 0 0831
294 CL0  0 374  0.7381 0 9175
295 S0   0 488  1 0   1 0
296 PLES 0 50   0 25  0 25
297 ,
298
299 *UNITS FOR WASTE WATER AND SOLID WASTE ARE TON PER '90 YUAN, AND
300 *UNIT FOR SMOG DUST IS TON PER 10,000 '90 YUAN IN D & DC MATRICES BELOW
```

```
301 TABLE D(G,I) PRODUCTION POLLUTION INTENSITY
302   AG MN   LG   EN   HE   CS   SV WA SD SW
303 WA 0.00 0 02078 0 00849 0.01792 0 00962 0 00000 0 00 0 00 0 00 0 00
304 SD 0 00 0.05608 0 01618 0 26223 0 01751 0 00000 0 00 0 00 0 00 0 00
305 SW 0 00 0 00266 0 00005 0 00053 0 00014 0 00000 0 00 0 00 0 00 0 00
306 ,
307
308 TABLE DC(G,I) CONSUMPTION POLLUTION INTENSITY (UNIT SAME AS ABOVE)
309   AG MN   LG   EN   HE   CS   SV WA SD SW
310 WA 0.00 0 02078 0 00849 0 01792 0 00962 0 00000 0 00 0 00 0 00 0 00
311 SD 0 00 0 05608 0 01618 0.26223 0 01751 0 00000 0 00 0 00 0 00 0 00
312 SW 0 00 0 00266 0.00005 0 00053 0 00014 0 00000 0 00 0 00 0.00 0 00
313 ;
314
315 TABLE  PETAX0(G,I) POLLUTION EMISSION TAXES ('90 Y 100 MILLION)
316    AG  MN  LG  EN  HE  CS  SV  WA  SD  SW
317 WA 0 00 0 17 3 20 0 37 5 78 0.00 0.00 0 0 0 0 0 0
318 SD 0.00 0 08 0.62 0 14 1.40 0 00 0 00 0 0 0 0 0 0
319 SW 0.00 0 02 0 07 0.06 0 16 0 00 0 00 0 0 0 0 0 0
320 ;
321
322 TABLE PACOST0(I,J) POLLUTION ABATEMENT PAYMENTS ('90 Y 100 MILLION)
323    AG  MN  LG  EN  HE  CS  SV  WA   SD   SW
324 WA 0 00  1.14  3.47  1 95  11 77 0 00 0 00  0 00  0 00  0 00
325 SD 0 00  0 27  0 57  2 48  1 86  0 00 0 00  0 00  0 00  0 00
326 SW 0 00  2 32  0 32  0.92  2 73  0 00 0 00  0.00  0 00  0 00
327 ,
328
329 *##### INITIAL VALUES ASSIGNMENT AND END PARAMETER COMPUTATION #####
330
331 M0(I)=ZZ("M0",I);
332 E0(I)=ZZ("E0",I);
333 CD0(I)=ZZ("CD0",I);
334
335 *DEFINE TRADABLE AND NON-TRADABLE SECTORS
336 IE(I)=YES$E0(I);
337 IEN(I)=NOT IE(I);
338 IM(I)=YES$M0(I);
339 IMN(I)=NOT IM(I);
340 IC(I)=YES$CD0(I);
341
342 MC0(I)=ZZ("MC0",I);
343 EC0(I)=ZZ("EC0",I);
344 XD0(I)=ZZ("XD0",I);
345 PD0(I)=ZZ("PD0",I);
346 PM0(I)=PD0(I);
347 PE0(I)=PD0(I);
348 PX0(I)=PD0(I);
349 P0(I)=PD0(I);
350 PK0(I)=SUM(J, P0(J)*BB(J,I));
351 L0(I)=ZZ("L0",I);
352 K0(I)=ZZ("K0",I);
353 KS0=SUM(I,K0(I));
354 WL0=SUM(I,ZZ("LBINC",I))/SUM(I, L0(I));
355 WK0=SUM(I,ZZ("KINC",I)+ZZ("DEPR",I))/SUM(I, K0(I));
356 WLDIST(I)=ZZ("LBINC",I)/L0(I)/WL0;
357 WKDIST(I)=(ZZ("KINC",I)+ZZ("DEPR",I))/K0(I)/WK0;
358 XLLB(I)=L0(I)+(1-SIGN(L0(I)));
359 LS0=SUM(I, L0(I))/(1-RUNEMP0);
360
361 *DISPLAY WLDIST. WKDIST;
362
363 CDTOT0=SUM(I, CD0(I));
```

126

```
364  SUB0(I)=ZZ("SUB0",I);
365  CSUB0=SUM(IP, SUB0(IP));
366  GD0(I)=ZZ("GD0",I);
367  GDTOT0=SUM(I, GD0(I));
368  DEPR(I)=ZZ("DEPR",I)/(PK0(I)*K0(I));
369  ITAX(I)=ZZ("ITAX",I)/XD0(I);
370  CLES(I)=CD0(I)/CDTOT0;
371  GLES(I)=GD0(I)/GDTOT0;
372  DST0(I)=ZZ("DST0",I);
373  DSTR(I)=DST0(I)/XD0(I);
374  AMC(I)=MC0(I)/XD0(I);
375  AEC(I)=EC0(I)/XD0(I);
376
377  TM0(IM)=ZZ("TRF0",IM)/(PM0(IM)*M0(IM));
378  TM0(IMN)=0;
379  TE(I)=ZZ("TE0",I);
380  PWM0(I)=PM0(I)/((1+TM0(I))*ER0);
381  PWE0(I)=PE0(I)/((1+TE(I))*ER0);
382  PVA0(I)=PX0(I)*(1-ITAX(I))+SUB0(I)/XD0(I)-SUM(JP, IO(JP,I)*P0(JP))
383  -SUM(G,PETAX0(G,I))/XD0(I)-SUM(G,PACOST0(G,I))/XD0(I);
384  XXD0(I)=XD0(I)-EC0(I)-E0(I);
385  INT0(IP)=SUM(J,IO(IP,J)*XD0(J)); INT0(IA)=SUM(J,PACOST0(IA,J))/P0(IA);
386  KIO(I)=ZZ("KIO",I);
387  ID0(I)=ZZ("ID0",I); IDE0(I)=ZZ("IDE0",I);
388  LBINC0=SUM(I,WLDIST(I)*WL0*L0(I));
389  YC0=SUM(I,WKDIST(I)*WK0*K0(I));
390  Y0=LBINC0+YC0;
391  TARIFF0=SUM(IM, TM0(IM)*M0(IM)*PM0(IM));
392  EXPSUB0=SUM(IE, TE(IE)*E0(IE)*PE0(IE));
393  INDTAX0=SUM(I, ITAX(I)*PX0(I)*XD0(I));
394
395  D("SD",I)=D("SD",I)/10000; DC("SD",I)=DC("SD",I)/10000;
396  TPE0(G)=DD("TPE0",G); TPD0(G)=DD("TPD0",G);
397  KIOE0(G)=DD("KIOE0",G);
398  REC0(G)=DD("REC0",G);
399  CL0(G)=DD("CL0",G);
400  S(G)=DD("S0",G);
401  PLES(G)=DD("PLES",G);
402  ETAX0=SUM(I, SUM(G, PETAX0(G,I)));
403  DSUB0=SUM(IA, SUB0(IA));
404  TD(G,I)=D(G,I)+(1-SIGN(D(G,I)));
405  DG0(G)=SUM(I, D(G,I)*XD0(I))+SUM(I,DC(G,I)*(CD0(I)+GD0(I)));
406  DA0(G)=SUM(I,D(G,I)*XD0(I))*S(G)*CL0(G);
407  TDA0(G)=DA0(G);
408  PA0(IA)=(XD0(IA)/TDA0(IA))*PX0(IA);
409  DE0(G)=DG0(G)-TDA0(G);
410  DCOMP0(G)=REC0(G)*(DG0(G)*S(G)-TDA0(G));
411  DCOMPEN0=SUM(G,DCOMP0(G));
412  DTAX0=SUM(G,TPD0(G)*SUM(IP, DC(G,IP)*CD0(IP)));
413  GDPVA0=SUM(I, PVA0(I)*XD0(I))+TARIFF0+INDTAX0+ETAX0-EXPSUB0-CSUB0-DSUB0;
414  RGDP0=SUM(I, CD0(I)+GD0(I)+ID0(I)+IDE0(I)+DST0(I))
415  +SUM(IE, E0(IE))+SUM(I,EC0(I))-SUM(IM,(1-TM0(IM))*M0(IM))-SUM(I,MC0(I));
416  PINDEX0=GDPVA0/RGDP0;
417  UTILITY0=SUM(G,PLES(G)*LOG(TDA0(G)))+SUM(IC,CLES(IC)*LOG(CD0(IC)));
418
419  *##### PARAMETER CALIBRATION #####
420
421  *ADJUSTMENT FACTORS IN POLLUTION EMISSION AND ABATEMENT COSTS
422
423  IMPL0(G,I)=PETAX0(G,I)/(TPE0(G)*TD(G,I)*XD0(I)*S(G)*(1-CL0(G)));
424  ADJ(G,I)=PACOST0(G,I)/(PA0(G)*TD(G,I)*XD0(I)*S(G)*CL0(G));
425
426  *DISPLAY IMPL0, ADJ;
```

427
428 * GET SHIFT AND SHARE PARAMETERS IN ARMINGTON FUNCTION
429
430 RHOC(I)=(1/ZZ("RHOC",I))-1;
431 DELTA(IM)$M0(IM)=PM0(IM)/PD0(IM)*(M0(IM)/(XXD0(IM)
432 +MC0(IM)))**(1+RHOC(IM));
433 DELTA(IM)=DELTA(IM)/(1+DELTA(IM));
434 X0(I)=PD0(I)*(XXD0(I)+MC0(I))+(PM0(I)*M0(I)*(1+TM0(I)))$IM(I);
435 AC(IM)=X0(IM)/(DELTA(IM)*M0(IM)**(-RHOC(IM))+(1-
436 DELTA(IM))*(XXD0(IM)+MC0(IM))**(-RHOC(IM)))**(-1/RHOC(IM));
437
438 * GET SHIFT AND SHARE PARAMETERS IN CET FUNCTION
439
440 RHOT(I)=(1/ZZ("RHOT",I))+1;
441 GAMMA(IE)=1/(1+PD0(IE)/PE0(IE)*(E0(IE)/(XXD0(IE)+EC0(IE)))**(RHOT(IE)-1));
442 AT(IE)=XD0(IE)/(GAMMA(IE)*E0(IE)**RHOT(IE)+(1-
443 GAMMA(IE))*(XXD0(IE)+EC0(IE))**RHOT(IE))**(1/RHOT(IE));
444
445 * GET ALPHA AND TECHNOLOGY COEFFICIENT IN PRODUCTION FUNCTION
446
447 ALPHL(I)=(WLDIST(I)*WL0*L0(I))/(PVA0(I)*XD0(I));
448 QD(I)=(XLLB(I)**ALPHL(I))*(K0(I)**(1-ALPHL(I)));
449 AD(I)=XD0(I)/QD(I);
450 LD=SUM(I,(XD0(I)*PVA0(I)*ALPHL(I)/(WLDIST(I)*WL0))$WLDIST(I));
451
452 *DISPLAY AC, DELTA, RHOC,
453 *DISPLAY AT, GAMMA, RHOT;
454 *DISPLAY ALPHL, AD, LD;
455
456 *##### VARIABLES DECLARATION #####
457
458 VARIABLES
459
460 *PRICES BLOCK
461 PD(I) DOMESTIC PRICES (UNITY)
462 PM(I) DOMESTIC PRICE OF IMPORTS (UNITY)
463 PE(I) DOMESTIC PRICE OF EXPORTS (UNITY)
464 PK(I) RATE OF CAPITAL RENT BY SECTOR (UNITY)
465 PX(I) AVERAGE OUTPUT PRICE BY SECTOR (UNITY)
466 P(I)   PRICE OF COMPOSITE GOODS (UNITY)
467 PVA(I) VALUE ADDED PRICE BY SECTOR (UNITY)
468 PWM(I) WORLD MARKET PRICE OF IMPORTS (UNITY)
469 PWE(I) WORLD MARKET PRICE OF EXPORTS (UNITY)
470 ER   REAL EXCHANGE RATE ('90 YUAN PER '90 U S DALLOR)
471 PINDEX GDP DEFLATOR (UNITY)
472 TM(I) TARIFF RATE (UNITLESS)
473 *PRODUCTION BLOCK
474 X(I)   COMPOSITE GOODS SUPPLY ('90 Y 100 MILLION)
475 XD(I) DOMESTIC OUTPUT BY SECTOR ('90 Y 100 MILLION)
476 XXD(I) DOMESTIC SALES ('90 Y 100 MILLION)
477 E(I)   EXPORTS BY SECTOR ('90 Y 100 MILLION)
478 M(I)   IMPORTS ('90 Y 100 MILLION)
479 EC(I) EXPORT TO ROC ('90 Y 100 MILLION)
480 MC(I) IMPORT FROM ROC ('90 Y 100 MILLION)
481 *FACTORS BLOCK
482 K(I)   CAPITAL STOCK BY SECTOR ('90 Y 100 MILLION)
483 WL AVERAGE WAGE RATE (CURR Y 100 MILLION PER MILLION PERSONS)
484 WK AVERAGE CAPITAL RETURN (UNITLESS)
485 LS LABOR SUPPLY (MILLION PERSONS)
486 KS CAPITAL SUPPLY ('90 Y 100 MILLION)
487 RUNEMP UNEMPLOYMENT RATE (UNITLESS)
488 L(I) EMPLOYMENT BY SECTOR (MILLION PERSONS)
489 *DEMAND BLOCK

490 INT(I) INTERMEDIATES USES ('90 Y 100 MILLION)
491 CD(I) FINAL DEMAND FOR PRIVATE CONSUMPTION ('90 Y 100 MILLION)
492 GD(I) FINAL DEMAND FOR GOVERNMENT CONSUMPTION ('90 Y 100 MILLION)
493 ID(I) FINAL DEMAND FOR PRODUCTIVE INVESTMENT ('90 Y 100 MILLION)
494 DST(I) INVENTORY INVESTMENT BY SECTOR ('90 Y 100 MILLION)
495 *INCOME, TAX, SUBSIDY, SAVING AND INVESTMENT
496 Y   TOTAL VALUE-ADDED (CURR Y 100 MILLION)
497 LBINC   PERSONAL INCOME (CURR Y 100 MILLION)
498 YC   COMPANY REVENUE (CURR Y 100 MILLION)
499 TYC % OF COMPANY REVENUE TRANSFER TO GOVERNMENT (UNITLESS)
500 TYH   PRIVATE INCOME TAX RATE (UNITLESS)
501 REMIT HOUSEHOLD INCOME FROM ROW (CURR Y 100 MILLION)
502 YCTAX TRANSFER OF COMPANY REVENUE TO GOVERNMENT (CURR Y 100 MILLION)
503 LBINCTAX PERSONAL INCOME TAX (CURR Y 100 MILLION)
504 GR   GOVERNMENT REVENUE   (CURR Y 100 MILLION)
505 TARIFF TARIFF REVENUE   (CURR Y 100 MILLION)
506 INDTAX INDIRECT TAX REVENUE   (CURR Y 100 MILLION)
507 SUB(I) GOV'T SUBSIDY TO ENTERPRISE BY SECTOR (CURR Y 100 MILLION)
508 EXPSUB EXPORT SUBSIDY (CURR Y 100 MILLION)
509 GADJ   INTRAGOVERNMENT TRANSFER (CURR Y 100 MILLION)
510 HSUB   GOVERNMENT SUBSIDY TO HOUSEHOLD (CURR Y 100 MILLION)
511 CSUB   GOVERNMENT SUBSIDY TO COMPONY (CURR Y 100 MILLION)
512 GDTOT   TOTAL VOLUME OF GOVERNMENT CONSUMPTION ('90 Y 100 MILLION)
513 MPS   MARGINAL PROPENSITY TO SAVE (UNITLESS)
514 HHSAV TOTAL HOUSEHOLD SAVING (CURR Y 100 MILLION)
515 CSAV   TOTAL COMPANY SAVING (CURR Y 100 MILLION)
516 GSAV GOVERNMENT SAVING (CURR Y 100 MILLION)
517 FDEBT GOVERNMENT DEBT INCOME (CURR Y 100 MILLION)
518 DDEBT GOVERNMENT DEBT PAYMENT (CURR Y 100 MILLION)
519 DEFICIT GOVERNMENT BUDGET DEFICIT (CURR Y 100 MILLION)
520 DEPRECIA TOTAL DEPRECIATION EXPENDITURE (CURR Y 100 MILLION)
521 INVEST TOTAL INVESTMENT (CURR Y 100 MILLION)
522 SAVING TOTAL SAVING (CURR Y 100 MILLION)
523 ROCSAV SAVING BY ROC (CURR Y 100 MILLION)
524 INVROC INVESTMENT TO ROC (CURR Y 100 MILLION)
525 BSPLUS SURPLUS IN BALANCE OF PAYMENT (CURR Y 100 MILLION)
526 DK(I) INVESTMENT BY SECTOR OF DESTINATION ('90 Y 100 MILLION)
527 GDPVA   NOMINAL GDP IN MARKET PRICES (CURR Y 100 MILLION)
528 RGDP   REAL GDP ('90 Y 100 MILLION)
529 *POLLUTION BLOCK
530 EINV ENVIRONMENTAL INVESTMENT (CURR Y 100 MILLION)
531 KIOE(IA) SHARE OF ENV INVESTMENT BY POLLUTION ABATEMENT SECTOR (UNITLESS)
532 DKE(I) ENV INVESTMENT BY SECTOR OF DESTINATION ('90 Y 100 MILLION)
533 IDE(I) FINAL DEMAND FOR ENVIRONMENTAL INVESTMENT ('90 Y 100 MILLION)
534 PETAX(G,I) POLLUTION EMISSION TAXES (CURR Y 100 MILLION)
535 PACOST(I,J) POLLUTION ABATEMENT PAYMENTS (CURR Y 100 MILLION)
536 TPE(G) TAX RATE ON PRODUCTION POLLUTION EMISSION (CURR YUAN PER TON)
537 TPD(G) TAX RATE ON HOUSEHOLD WASTE DISPOSAL (CURR YUAN PER TON)
538 ETAX   TOTAL POLLUTION EMISSION TAX REVENUE (CURR Y 100 MILLION)
539 DTAX   TOTAL HOUSEHOLD POLLUTION DISPOSAL TAX (CURR Y 100 MILLION)
540 DSUB GOVERNMENT SUBSIDY TO POLLUTION CONTROL (CURR Y 100 MILLION)
541 REC(G) COEFFICIENT FOR POLLUTION COMPENSATION (CURR YUAN PER TON)
542 DCOMP(G) POLLUTION COMPENSATION FOR POLLUTION G (CURR YUAN PER TON)
543 DCOMPEN TOTAL COMPENSATION FOR POLLUTION DAMAGE (CURR Y 100 MILLION)
544 CL(G) PERCENTAGE OF POLLUTANT ABATED (UNITLESS)
545 IMPL(G,I) ADJUSTMENT PARAMETER FOR EMISSION TAX IMPLEMENTATION (UNITLESS)
546 PA(IA) PRICE(OR AVERAGE COST) OF POLLUTANT ABATED (CURR YUAN PER TON)
547 DA(IA) POLLUTANT ABATED BY POLLUTANT AND BY SECTOR (100 MILLION TONS)
548 TDA(IA) TOTAL POLLUTANT ABATED BY POLLUTANT (100 MILLION TONS)
549 DG(G) TOTAL AMOUNT OF POLLUTION GENERATION BY POLLUTANT (100 MILLION TONS)
550 DE(G) TOTAL AMOUNT OF POLLUTION DISCHARGED (100 MILLION TONS)
551 *WELFARE INDICATOR FOR OBJECTIVE FUNCTION
552 OMEGA OBJECTIVE FUNCTION VARIABLE ('90 Y 100 MILLION)

553 UTILITY THE VALUE OF SOCIAL WELFARE FUNCTION
554 * SLACK VARIABLES FOR CHECKING FOR BASE YEAR RUN
555 WAL(I) SLACK VARIABLES
556 ,
557
558 *##### VARIABLE BOUNDS #####
559
560 P LO(I)= 001; PD.LO(I)= 001; PM LO(IM) = 001; PWE LO(IE)= 001;
561 PK LO(I)= 001; PX LO(I)= 01;
562 X LO(I)= 01; XD.LO(IP)= 01; XXD.LO(I)= 01;
563 XD.LO(IA)=XD0(IA);
564 E LO(IE)= 01; M.LO(IM)= 01;
565 CD.L(IC)=0.01; ID LO(I)=0; IDE LO(I)=0;
566 L LO(I)=.01; RUNEMP LO=0; K LO(I)= 01;
567 CSAV LO=0; GSAV LO=0; HHSAV LO=0;
568 PETAX.LO(G,I)=0; PACOST LO(I,J)=0:
569 DTAX.LO=0;
570 TDA.LO(G)=0 01; DE.LO(G)=0.001;
571
572 *##### EQUATION DEFINITION #####
573
574 EQUATIONS
575 *PRICE BLOCK
576 PEDEF(I) DEFINITION OF DOMESTIC EXPORT PRICES (UNITY)
577 PMDEF(I) DEFINITION OF DOMESTIC IMPORT PRICES (UNITY)
578 SALES(I) VALUE OF DOMESTIC OUTPUT (CURR Y 100 MILLION)
579 ABSORPTION(I) VALUE OF DOMESTIC SALES (CURR Y 100 MILLION)
580 ACTCOST(I) DECOMPOSITION OF ACTIVITY COSTS (CURR Y 100 MILLION)
581 PKDEF(I) DEFINITION OF CAPITAL GOODS PRICE (UNITY)
582 PINDEXDEF DEFINITION OF GENERAL PRICE LEVEL (UNITY)
583 *OUTPUT BLOCK
584 ACTIVITY(I) PRODUCTION FUNCTION   ('90 Y 100 MILLION)
585 LBDEMAND(I) OPTIMAL LABOR DEMAND(FOC) (MILLION PERSONS)
586 KDEMAND(I) OPTIMAL CAPITAL DEMAND(FOC) ('90 Y 100 MILLION)
587 CET1(I) CET FUNCTION FOR EXPORT SECTOR ('90 Y 100 MILLION)
588 CET2(I) CET FUNCTION FOR NONEXPORT SECOTR ('90 Y 100 MILLION)
589 EXPSUPPLY(I) EXPORT SUPPLY ('90 Y 100 MILLION)
590 ARMINGTON1(I) COMPOSITE GOOD AGGREGATION FUNCTION ('90 Y 100 MILLION)
591 ARMINGTON2(I) FOR NON-IMPORT SECTOR ('90 Y 100 MILLION)
592 IMPDEMAND(I) IMPORT DEMAND ('90 Y 100 MILLION)
593 EROC(I) EXPORT TO ROC ('90 Y 100 MILLION)
594 MROC(I) IMPORT FROM ROC ('90 Y 100 MILLION)
595 *INCOME AND SAVING BLOCK
596 GDP PERSONAL AND COMPANY INCOME (CURR Y 100 MILLION)
597 HHINCOME PERSONAL INCOME (CURR Y 100 MILLION)
598 CINCOME COMPANY REVENUE (CURR Y 100 MILLION)
599 HHINCTAX PERSONAL INCOME TAX (CURR Y 100 MILLION)
600 CINCOMETAX TRANSFER OF COMPANY REVENUE TO GOVERNMENT
                                    (CURR Y 100 MILLION)
601 HHSAVEQ HOUSEHOLD SAVING (CURR Y 100 MILLION)
602 CSAVING COMPANY REVENUE EQUATION (CURR Y 100 MILLION)
603 TARIFFDEF TARIFF REVENUE (CURR Y 100 MILLION)
604 INDTAXDEF INDIRECT TAXES ON DOMESTIC PRODUCTION (CURR Y 100 MILLION)
605 ENTSUBSIDY GOVERNMENT SUBSIDY TO ENTERPRISES (CURR Y 100 MILLION)
606 EXPSUBSIDY EXPORT DUTIES   (CURR Y 100 MILLION)
607 GREQ   GOVERNMENT REVENUE   (CURR Y 100 MILLION)
608 GSAVING GOVERNMENT SAVING   (CURR Y 100 MILLION)
609 DEPREQ DEPRECIATION EXPENDITURE (CURR Y 100 MILLION)
610 TOTSAV TOTAL SAVING   (CURR Y 100 MILLION)
611 *DEMAND BLOCK
612 CDEQ(I) PRIVATE CONSUMPTION BEHAVIOR ('90 Y 100 MILLION)
613 GDEQ(I) GOVERNMENT CONSUMPTION BEHAVIOR ('90 Y 100 MILLION)
614 INTEQ1(J) INTERMEDIATE GOODS OF PRODUCTION SECTORS ('90 Y 100 MILLION)

615 INTEQ2(J) INTERMEDIATE GOODS OF ABATEMENT SECTORS ('90 Y 100 MILLION)
616 DSTEQ(I) INVENTORY INVESTMENT ('90 Y 100 MILLION)
617 PRODINV(I) INVESTMENT BY SECTOR OF DESTINATION ('90 Y 100 MILLION)
618 IEQ(I) INVESTMENT BY SECTOR OF ORIGIN ('90 Y 100 MILLION)
619 *GROSS NATIONAL PRODUCT
620 GDPVADEF NOMINAL GDP DEFINITION (CURR Y 100 MILLION)
621 RGDPDEF REAL GDP DEFINITION ('90 Y 100 MILLION)
622 *POLLUTION BLOCK
623 PRODEINV(I) ENV INVEST BY SECTOR OF DESTINATION ('90 Y 100 MILLION)
624 IDEEQ(I) ENV INVEST BY SECTOR OF ORIGIN ('90 Y 100 MILLION)
625 PETAXEQ(G,I) POLLUTION EMISSION TAXES ('90 Y 100 MILLION)
626 PACOSTEQ(IA,I) POLLUTION ABATEMENT PAYMENTS ('90 Y 100 MILLION)
627 PAPRICE(IA) CONVERSION OF PRICE FOR POLLUTANT ABATED (CURR YUAN PER TONS)
628 PABATED(IA) POLLUTION ABATEMENT BY POLLUTANT (100 MILLION TONS)
629 RCLNUP(G) POLLUTION CLEANUP RATE BY POLLUTANTS (UNITLESS)
630 TPABATED(IA) POLLUTANT ABATEMENT BY POLLUTANT (100 MILLION TONS)
631 PGENERATED(G) POLLUTION GENERATION BY POLLUTANT (100 MILLION TONS)
632 DEMITTED(G) POLLUTION DISCHARGE BY POLLUTANT (100 MILLION TONS)
633 ETAXEQ TOTAL POLLUTION EMISSION TAX REVENU (CURR Y 100 MILLION)
634 POCTRLSUB POLLUTION CONTROL SUBSIDY (CURR Y 100 MILLION)
635 DTAXEQ HOUSEHOLD POLLUTION DISPOSAL TAX (CURR Y 100 MILLION)
636 PCOMP(G) POLLUTION COMPENSATION BY POLLUTANT (CURR Y 100 MILLION)
637 PCOMPEN TOTAL POLLUTION COMPENSATION (CURR Y 100 MILLION)
638 *MARKET CLEARING
639 EQUIL(I) GOODS MARKET EQUILIBRIUM ('90 Y 100 MILLION)
640 LMEQUIL LABOR MARKET EQUILIBRIUM (MILLION PERSONS)
641 KMEQUIL CAPITAL MARKET EQUILBRIUM ('90 Y 100 MILLION)
642 CAEQ CURRENT ACCOUNT BALANCE (CURR Y 100 MILLION)
643 * SAVINVEQ SAVING-INVESTMENT EQUATION
644 *OBJECTIVE FUNCTION
645 OBJ OBJECTIVE FUNCTION ('90 Y 100 MILLION)
646 UTILITYFN SOCIAL WELFARE FUNCTION
647 ,
648
649 *##### EQUATION ASSIGNMENT #####
650
651 *PRICE BLOCK
652 PEDEF(IE). PE(IE) =E= PWE(IE)*ER*(1+TE(IE));
653 PMDEF(IM) PM(IM) =E= PWM(IM)*ER*(1+TM(IM));
654 SALES(I) PX(I)*XD(I) =E= PD(I)*(XXD(I)+EC(I))+(PE(I)*E(I))$IE(I);
655 ABSORPTION(I) . P(I)*X(I) =E= PD(I)*(XXD(I)+MC(I))
656 +(PM(I)*M(I)*(1+TM(I)))$IM(I);
657 ACTCOST(I) PVA(I)*XD(I) =E= PX(I)*XD(I)*(1-ITAX(I))+SUB(I)
658 -SUM(JP,IO(JP,I)*P(JP))*XD(I)-SUM(G,PETAX(G,I))-SUM(G,PACOST(G,I));
659 PKDEF(I) PK(I) =E= SUM(J,P(J)*BB(J,I));
660 PINDEXDEF PINDEX =E= GDPVA/RGDP;
661
662 *OUTPUT AND FACTORS OF PRODUCTION BLOCK
663
664 ACTIVITY(I) XD(I) =E= AD(I)*L(I)**ALPHL(I)*K(I)**(1-ALPHL(I));
665 LBDEMAND(I)$WLDIST(I) WL*WLDIST(I)*L(I)=E=XD(I)*PVA(I)*ALPHL(I);
666 KDEMAND(I)$WKDIST(I) WK*WKDIST(I)*K(I)=E=XD(I)*PVA(I)*(1-ALPHL(I));
667 CET1(IE) XD(IE) =E= AT(IE)*(GAMMA(IE)*E(IE)**RHOT(IE)+(1-
668 GAMMA(IE))*(XXD(IE)+EC(IE))**RHOT(IE))**(1/RHOT(IE));
669 CET2(IEN).. XXD(IEN) =E= XD(IEN);
670 EXPSUPPLY(IE) E(IE)/(XXD(IE)+EC(IE)) =E= (PE(IE)/PD(IE)*(1-
671 GAMMA(IE))/GAMMA(IE))**(1/(RHOT(IE)-1));
672 ARMINGTON1(IM) X(IM)=E=AC(IM)*(DELTA(IM)*M(IM)**(-RHOC(IM))+(1-
673 DELTA(IM))*(XXD(IM)+MC(IM))**(-RHOC(IM)))**(-1/RHOC(IM));
674 ARMINGTON2(IMN) X(IMN) =E= XXD(IMN);
675 IMPDEMAND(IM). M(IM)/(XXD(IM)+MC(IM)) =E= (PD(IM)/PM(IM)*DELTA(IM)/(1-
676 DELTA(IM)))**(1/(1+RHOC(IM)));
677 EROC(I). EC(I) =E= AEC(I)*XD(I);

131

678 MROC(I). MC(I) =E= AMC(I)*XD(I);
679
680 *INCOME AND SAVING BLOCK
681 GDP Y =E= LBINC+YC,
682 HHINCOME LBINC =E= SUM(I,WLDIST(I)*WL*L(I));
683 CINCOME YC =E= SUM(I,WKDIST(I)*WK*K(I));
684 HHINCTAX. LBINCTAX =E= LBINC*TYH;
685 CINCOMETAX YCTAX =E= (YC-DEPRECIA)*TYC,
686 HHSAVEQ . HHSAV =E= MPS*((1-TYH)*LBINC+REMIT+DCOMPEN-DTAX-DDEBT);
687 CSAVING CSAV =E= YC-DEPRECIA-YCTAX-DCOMPEN;
688 TARIFFDEF TARIFF =E= SUM(IM, TM(IM)*M(IM)*PM(IM));
689 INDTAXDEF INDTAX =E= SUM(I, ITAX(I)*PX(I)*XD(I));
690 ENTSUBSIDY CSUB =E= SUM(IP,SUB(IP));
691 EXPSUBSIDY EXPSUB =E= SUM(IE, TE(IE)*E(IE)*PE(IE));
692 GREQ. GR =E= LBINCTAX+YCTAX+TARIFF+INDTAX+ETAX+DTAX
693 +FDEBT+DDEBT+GADJ;
694 GSAVING GSAV =E= GR-SUM(I, P(I)*GD(I))-HSUB-CSUB-DSUB-EXPSUB+DEFICIT;
695 DEPREQ DEPRECIA =E= SUM(I, DEPR(I)*PK(I)*K(I));
696 TOTSAV SAVING =E= HHSAV+CSAV+DEPRECIA+GSAV+ROCSAV-DEFICIT;
697
698 *EXPENDITURE BLOCK
699 CDEQ(I) P(I)*CD(I) =E= CLES(I)*((LBINC*(1-TYH)+REMIT-DDEBT
700 +DCOMPEN-DTAX)*(1-MPS)+HSUB);
701 GDEQ(I) . GD(I) =E= GLES(I)*GDTOT;
702 INTEQ1(JP) INT(JP) =E= SUM(I,IO(JP,I)*XD(I));
703 INTEQ2(IA) INT(IA) =E= SUM(I,PACOST(IA,I)/P(IA));
704 DSTEQ(I) DST(I) =E= DSTR(I)*XD(I);
705 PRODINV(IP) PK(IP)*DK(IP) =E= KIO(IP)*(INVEST-EINV-INVROC
706 -BSPLUS-SUM(J,P(J)*DST(J)));
707 IEQ(I) ID(I) =E= SUM(IP, BB(I,IP)*DK(IP));
708
709 *GROSS NATIONAL PRODUCT
710 GDPVADEF . GDPVA =E= SUM(I, PVA(I)*XD(I))+TARIFF+INDTAX+ETAX-EXPSUB
711 -CSUB-DSUB;
712 RGDPDEF RGDP =E= SUM(I, CD(I)+GD(I)+ID(I)+IDE(I)+DST(I))+SUM(IE,E(IE))
713 +SUM(I,EC(I))-SUM(IM,(1-TM(IM))*M(IM))-SUM(I,MC(I));
714
715 *POLLUTION BLOCK
716 PRODEINV(IA). PK(IA)*DKE(IA) =E= KIOE(IA)*EINV;
717 IDEEQ(I) IDE(I) =E= SUM(IA, BB(I,IA)*DKE(IA));
718 PETAXEQ(G,I).. PETAX(G,I)=E=TPE(G)*D(G,I)*XD(I)*S(G)*(1-CL(G))*IMPL(G,I);
719 PACOSTEQ(IA,I) PACOST(IA,I)=E=PA(IA)*D(IA,I)*XD(I)*S(IA)*CL(IA)*ADJ(IA,I);
720 PAPRICE(IA) PA(IA) =E= (XD0(IA)/TDA0(IA))*PX(IA);
721 PABATED(IA) DA(IA) =E= TDA(IA)-GD(IA)*TDA0(IA)/XD0(IA);
722 RCLNUP(G) CL(G) =E= DA(G)/(SUM(I,D(G,I)*XD(I))*S(G));
723 TPABATED(IA) . TDA(IA) =E= XD(IA)*TDA0(IA)/XD0(IA);
724 PGENERATED(G).. DG(G) =E= SUM(I, D(G,I)*XD(I))
725 +SUM(I,DC(G,I)*(CD(I)+GD(I)));
726 DEMITTED(G) . DE(G) =E= DG(G)-TDA(G);
727 ETAXEQ ETAX =E= SUM(I, SUM(G, PETAX(G,I)));
728 POCTRLSUB.. DSUB =E= SUM(IA, SUB(IA));
729 DTAXEQ. DTAX =E= SUM(G,TPD(G)*SUM(IP, DC(G,IP)*CD(IP)));
730 PCOMP(G) DCOMP(G) =E= REC(G)*(DG(G)*S(G)-TDA(G));
731 PCOMPEN.. DCOMPEN =E= SUM(G, DCOMP(G));
732
733 *MARKET CLEARING
734 EQUIL(I) X(I) =E= INT(I)+CD(I)+GD(I)+ID(I)+IDE(I)+DST(I)+WAL(I);
735 LMEQUIL. SUM(I, L(I)) =E= LS*(1-RUNEMP);
736 KMEQUIL SUM(I, K(I)) =E= KS;
737 CAEQ SUM(IM, PM(IM)*M(IM))+SUM(I,PD(I)*MC(I))+INVROC+BSPLUS =E=
738 SUM(IE,PE(IE)*E(IE))+SUM(I,PD(I)*EC(I))+ROCSAV+REMIT+FDEBT;
739 * SAVINVEQ . INVEST =E= SAVING;
740

```
741 *OBJECTIVE FUNCTION
742 OBJ.. OMEGA =E= SUM(I, WAL(I)*WAL(I));
743 UTILITYFN . UTILITY =E= SUM(G, PLES(G)*LOG(TDA(G)))
744 +SUM(IC, CLES(IC)*LOG(CD(IC)));
745
746 *##### VARIABLE INITIALIZATION #####
747
748 X L(I)=X0(I); XD L(I)=XD0(I); XXD L(I)=XXD0(I);
749 M L(I)=M0(I); E L(I)=E0(I); MC L(I)=MC0(I); EC L(I)=EC0(I);
750 CD.L(I)=CD0(I); GD.L(I)=GD0(I);
751 DST L(I)=DSTR(I)*XD0(I); INT L(I)=INT0(I);
752 DK.L(IP)=(SAVING0-EINV0-INVROC0-BSPLUS0-SUM(J,DST L(J)))*KIO(IP);
753 ID L(I)=SUM(IP, BB(I,IP)*DK L(IP));
754 PD.L(I)=PD0(I); PM L(I)=PM0(I); PE L(I)=PE0(I); P L(I)=PD0(I);
755 PX L(I)=PD0(I); PK L(I)=PD0(I);
756 PVA L(I)=PVA0(I); PWE L(I)=PWE0(I); PWM L(I)=PWM0(I);
757 WL L=WL0; WK.L=WK0; L L(I)= L0(I); K L(I)=K0(I);
758 RUNEMP.L=RUNEMP0;
759
760 Y L=Y0;
761 LBINC L=LBINC0;
762 YC.L=Y0-LBINC0;
763 DEPRECIA L=SUM(I, DEPR(I)*PK0(I)*K L(I));
764 YCTAX L=(YC L-DEPRECIA L)*TYC0; LBINCTAX L=LBINC L*TYH0;
765 TM L(I)=TM0(I);
766 TARIFF L=TARIFF0;
767 EXPSUB L=EXPSUB0;
768 INDTAX.L=INDTAX0;
769 GR.L=GR0;
770 CSUB.L=CSUB0; DSUB L=DSUB0;
771 CSAV.L=CSAV0;
772 HHSAV.L=MPS0*((1-TYH0)*LBINC L-DDEBT0+REMIT0+DCOMPEN0-DTAX0);
773 GSAV L=GSAV0;
774 BSPLUS.L=BSPLUS0;
775 SAVING.L=SAVING0; INVEST L=SAVING L,
776
777 PETAX L(G,I)=PETAX0(G,I); PACOST.L(G,I)=PACOST0(G,I);
778 ETAX.L=ETAX0;
779 PA.L(IA)=PA0(IA);
780 DA.L(IA)=DA0(IA); TDA L(G)=TDA0(G);
781 DG.L(G)=DG0(G); DE.L(G)=DE0(G);
782 DKE L(IA)=KIOE0(IA)*EINV0;
783 IDE L(I)=SUM(IA, BB(I,IA)*DKE L(IA));
784 DTAX.L=SUM(G,TPD0(G)*SUM(IP, DC(G,IP)*CD0(IP)));
785 DCOMP L(G)=DCOMP0(G);
786 DCOMPEN L=DCOMPEN0;
787 CL.L(IA)=CL0(IA);
788 INT.L(JP)=SUM(I,IO(JP,I)*XD0(I));
789 INT.L(IA)=SUM(J,PACOST0(IA,J))/P0(IA);
790 GDPVA.L=GDPVA0;
791 RGDP.L=RGDP0;
792 PINDEX.L=GDPVA0/RGDP0;
793 UTILITY L=UTILITY0;
794
795 *CONTROL VALUES FOR ENVIRONMENTAL POLICY SIMULATIONS
796
797 TABLE SIM1(*,I) VALUES FOR POLICY SIMULATIONS
798     AG   MN   LG   EN   HE   CS   SV   WA   SD   SW
799 SSUB 0.00 134 00 134.00 26.00 285 00 0 00 0 00 0 00 0 00
800 ;
801
802 TABLE SIM2(*,G) VALUES FOR ENVIRONMENTAL POLICY SIMULATIONS
803     WA   SD   SW
```

133

```
804 STPE  0 20   178 0  3 00
805 STPD  0 00   0 0   0 00
806 SKIOE 0 6335 0 2168 0 1497
807 SREC  0 0024 2 3104 0 0831
808 .
809
810 TABLE SIMPL(G,I) SIMULATION VALUES OF EMISSION TAX IMPLEMENT  FACTORS
811    AG  MN      LG     EN       HE       CS   SV
812 WA 0 0  0 07371860 0 57493604 0 17407504 0 58661916 0 0  0 0
813 SD 0 0  0 22384094 1 01782759 0 07837945 1 35934335 0 0  0 0
814 SW 0 0  0 05013080 1.58011170 0.70620480 0 82561568 0 0  0 0
815 .
816
817 *##### MODEL CLOSURE #####
818
819 *NUMERAIRE
820 PD FX("AG")=PD0("AG");
821 *PINDEX FX=PINDEX L,
822
823 *FIXED WORLD PRICES AND EXCHANGE RATE2
824 PWE FX(I)=PWE0(I);
825 PWM FX(I)=PWM0(I);
826 ER FX=ER0;
827
828 *EXOGENOUS FACTORS
829 LS FX=LS0;
830 KS FX=KS0;
831 WL FX=WL0;
832
833 *TAX RATES AND EXOGENOUS GOVERNMENT SPENDING
834 TYH.FX=TYH0;
835 TYC FX=TYC0;
836 TM FX(I)=TM0(I);
837 SUB FX(I)=SIM1("SSUB",I);
838 GADJ FX=GADJ0;
839 HSUB FX=HSUB0;
840 GDTOT FX=GDTOT0;
841
842 *FIXED SAVING RATE
843 MPS FX=MPS0;
844
845 *EXOGENOUS FOREIGN SAVING AND INVESTMENT
846 ROCSAV FX=ROCSAV0;
847 FDEBT FX=FDEBT0;
848 DDEBT FX=DDEBT0;
849 DEFICIT.FX=DEFICIT0;
850 REMIT.FX=REMIT0;
851 INVROC.FX=INVROC0;
852 *BSPLUS FX=BSPLUS0;
853
854 *EXOGENOUS POLLUTION CONTROL VARIABLES
855 *FOR ENVIRONMENTAL POLICY SIMULATIONS
856
857 *FIXED POLLUTION CLEANUP PRICES
858 *P.FX("WA")=P0("WA");
859
860 *ENVIRONMENTAL INVESTMENT
861 EINV FX=EINV0;
862 KIOE FX(IA)=SIM2("SKIOE",IA);
863
864 *POLLUTION TAX RATES AND IMPLEMENTATION FACTORS
865 TPE FX(G)=SIM2("STPE",G);
866 TPD FX(G)=SIM2("STPD",G);
```

```
867  IMPL FX(G,I)=IMPL0(G,I);
868
869  *ENVIRONMENTAL COMPENSATION RATE
870  REC.FX(G)=SIM2("SREC",G);
871
872  *EXOGENOUS CLEANUP RATES(THESE VARIABLES CAN BE CONVERTED INTO
873  *EMISSION PERMITS IF NECESSARY)
874  *CL FX("WA")= 4624;
875
876  *##### SOLVE THE MODEL #####
877
878  OPTIONS ITERLIM=5000, LIMROW=0, LIMCOL=0;
879  OPTIONS SOLPRINT=OFF;
880  OPTION DECIMALS=4;
881
882  MODEL CNECGE CHINA ENVIRONMENTAL CGE MODEL /ALL/;
883
884  CNECGE OPTFILE=1;
885
886  SOLVE CNECGE MINIMIZING OMEGA USING NLP;
887
888  *##### DISPLAY SOLUTIONS #####
889  TXD=SUM(IP,XD.L(IP));
890  TXD0=SUM(IP,XD0(IP));
891  TCD=SUM(IP,CD L(IP));
892  TCD0=SUM(IP,CD0(IP));
893
894  DISPLAY PX0, PX L, P0, P L, PVA0, PVA L, PK0, PK L,
895  DISPLAY PINDEX0, PINDEX L,
896  DISPLAY XD0, XD L, TXD0, TXD, X0, X L, XXD0, XXD L, E0, E L, M0, M L,
897  DISPLAY L0, L.L, K0, K L, RUNEMP0, RUNEMP L,
898  DISPLAY CD0, CD L, TCD0, TCD, GD0, GD L, INT0, INT L, ID0, ID L,
899  DISPLAY IDE0, IDE L, DST0, DST L,
900  DISPLAY Y0, Y L, WL0, WL L, WK0, WK L, LBINC0, LBINC L, YC0, YC L, GR0, GR L,
901  DISPLAY HHSAV0, HHSAV L, CSAV0, CSAV L, GSAV0, GSAV L,
902  DISPLAY SAVING0, SAVING.L, INVEST L,
903  DISPLAY BSPLUS0, BSPLUS L, DEFICIT0, DEFICIT L,
904  DISPLAY GDPVA0, GDPVA L, RGDP0, RGDP L,
905  DISPLAY PETAX0, PETAX L, IMPL0, IMPL L,
906  DISPLAY PACOST0, PACOST L, CL0, CL L,
907  DISPLAY PA0, PA L,
908  DISPLAY DA0, DA L, TDA0, TDA L, DG0, DG L, DE0, DE L,
909  DISPLAY ETAX0, ETAX L, DTAX0, DTAX L,
910  DISPLAY DSUB0, DSUB L, DCOMPEN0, DCOMPEN L,
911  DISPLAY UTILITY0, UTILITY.L, OMEGA L,
912  DISPLAY WAL L,
913
914  *##### END OF PROGRAM #####
915


COMPILATION TIME   =      1 050 SECONDS       VERID MW2-00-064

GAMS 2 25 064  386/486 DOS            07/18/95 10:22:14 PAGE    19

ENVIRONMENTAL CGE MODEL FOR CHINA, JIAN XIE, CORNELL UNIV
Model Statistics   SOLVE CNECGE USING NLP FROM LINE 886

MODEL STATISTICS

BLOCKS OF EQUATIONS    63    SINGLE EQUATIONS     318
BLOCKS OF VARIABLES    88    SINGLE VARIABLES     394
NON ZERO ELEMENTS    1792    NON LINEAR N-Z       992
DERIVATIVE POOL      63    CONSTANT POOL       222
```

135

CODE LENGTH   10881

GENERATION TIME   =   2 300 SECONDS
EXECUTION TIME   =   3 510 SECONDS   VERID MW2-00-064

S O L V E   S U M M A R Y

MODEL CNECGE   OBJECTIVE OMEGA
TYPE NLP   DIRECTION MINIMIZE
SOLVER MINOS5   FROM LINE 886

**** SOLVER STATUS   1 NORMAL COMPLETION
**** MODEL STATUS   2 LOCALLY OPTIMAL
**** OBJECTIVE VALUE   0 0000

RESOURCE USAGE, LIMIT   4 840   1000 000
ITERATION COUNT, LIMIT   138   5000
EVALUATION ERRORS   0   0

M I N O S   5 3   (Nov 1990)   Ver: 225-386-02
= = = = =

B A Murtagh, University of New South Wales, and
P E Gill, W Murray, M. A Saunders and M H Wright
Systems Optimization Laboratory, Stanford University

OPTIONS file
----
  begin
  start assigned nonlinears basic
  end

Work space allocated   --   0 43 Mb

EXIT -- OPTIMAL SOLUTION FOUND
MAJOR ITNS, LIMIT   7   200
FUNOBJ, FUNCON CALLS   51   53
SUPERBASICS   6
INTERPRETER USAGE   1 10
NORM RG / NORM PI   3 901E-09

**** REPORT SUMMARY   0   NONOPT
                 0 INFEASIBLE
                 0 UNBOUNDED
                 0   ERRORS

---- 894 VARIABLE PX L   AVERAGE OUTPUT PRICE BY SECTOR (UNITY)

AG 1 0000,   MN 1 0000,   LG 1 0000,   EN 1 0000,   HE 1 0000,   CS 1 0000
SV 1 0000,   WA 1 0000,   SD 1 0000,   SW 1 0000

---- 894 VARIABLE P.L   PRICE OF COMPOSITE GOODS (UNITY)

AG 1 0000,   MN 1 0000,   LG 1 0000,   EN 1 0000,   HE 1 0000,   CS 1 0000
SV 1.0000,   WA 1 0000,   SD 1 0000,   SW 1 0000

---- 894 PARAMETER PVA0   VALUE ADDED PRICE BY SECTOR (UNITY)

AG 0 6458,   MN 0 5030,   LG 0 1968,   EN 0 2848,   HE 0 2536,   CS 0 2724
SV 0 5604,   WA 0.3785,   SD 0 3035,   SW 0 3399

---- 894 VARIABLE PVA L   VALUE ADDED PRICE BY SECTOR (UNITY)

136

AG 0.6458,   MN 0.5030,   LG 0 1968,   EN 0 2848,   HE 0 2536,   CS 0 2724
SV 0 5604,   WA 0 3785,   SD 0 3035,   SW 0 3399

---- 894 VARIABLE PK L   RATE OF CAPITAL RENT BY SECTOR (UNITY)

AG 1 0000,   MN 1 0000,   LG 1 0000,   EN 1 0000,   HE 1 0000,   CS 1 0000
SV 1 0000,   WA 1 0000,   SD 1 0000,   SW 1 0000

---- 895 PARAMETER PINDEX0   =   0 9908 PRICE INDEX IN THE BASE YEAR (UNITY)
       VARIABLE PINDEX L   =   0 9908 GDP DEFLATOR (UNITY)

---- 896 PARAMETER XD0   VOLUME OF DOMESTIC OUTPUT BY SECTOR ('90 Y 100 MILLION)

AG 7659 9608,   MN 1366 9045,   LG 8074 8536,   EN 1460.9627
HE 12615 6150,   CS 3048.2097,   SV 7581 3666,   WA   18 3284
SD   5.1853,   SW   6 2835

---- 896 VARIABLE XD.L   DOMESTIC OUTPUT BY SECTOR ('90 Y 100 MILLION)

AG 7659 6482,   MN 1366 8963,   LG 8074 5473,   EN 1460 9957
HE 12615.4024,   CS 3048 2063,   SV 7581 1985,   WA   18 4798
SD   5 1853,   SW   6 2835

---- 896 PARAMETER TXD0   = 41807 8729 TOTAL DOMESTIC OUTPUT IN THE BASE YEAR
                                                   ('90 Y 100 MILLION)
       PARAMETER TXD   = 41806.8948 TOTAL DOMESTIC OUTPUT ('90 Y 100 MILLION)

---- 896 PARAMETER X0   VOLUME OF COMPOSITE GOOD SUPPLY ('90 Y 100 MILLION)

AG 7499 9608,   MN 1446.9045,   LG 7574 8536,   EN 1408.9627
HE 12989.6150,   CS 3048 2097,   SV 7434 3666,   WA   18 3284
SD   5.1853,   SW   6 2835

---- 896 VARIABLE X L   COMPOSITE GOODS SUPPLY ('90 Y 100 MILLION)

AG 7499.6547,   MN 1446 8963,   LG 7574 5704,   EN 1408 9949
HE 12989.4154,   CS 3048 2063,   SV ·7434 2017,   WA   18 4798
SD   5.1853,   SW   6 2835

---- 896 PARAMETER XXD0   VOLUME OF DOMESTIC SALES BY SECTOR
                                        ('90 Y 100 MILLION)

AG 7275.9608,   MN 993 9045,   LG 7217 8536,   EN 1408 9627
HE 11313 6150,   CS 3048 2097,   SV 7434 3666,   WA   18 3284
SD   5 1853,   SW   6 2835

---- 896 VARIABLE XXD L   DOMESTIC SALES ('90 Y 100 MILLION)

AG 7275.6638,   MN 993 8987,   LG 7217 5830,   EN 1408 9949
HE 11313.4344,   CS 3048 2063,   SV 7434 2017,   WA   18 4798
SD   5 1853,   SW   6.2835

---- 896 PARAMETER E0   VOLUME OF EXPORTS ('90 Y 100 MILLION)

AG 384 0000,   MN 373 0000,   LG 857 0000,   EN 52 0000
HE 1302 0000,   SV 147 0000

---- 896 VARIABLE E L   EXPORTS BY SECTOR ('90 Y 100 MILLION)

AG 383 9843,   MN 372 9976,   LG 856 9643,   EN 52 0008
HE 1301 9680,   SV 146 9968

---- 896 PARAMETER M0   VOLUME OF IMPORTS ('90 Y 100 MILLION)

AG 214 0000,   MN 443 0000,   LG 274 0000,   HE 1620 0000

---- 896 VARIABLE M L   IMPORTS ('90 Y 100 MILLION)

AG 213 9913,   MN 442 9976,   LG 273 9905,   HE 1619 9819

---- 897 PARAMETER L0   LABOR DEMAND BY SECTOR IN BASE YEAR
                          (MILLION PERSONS)
AG 341 7700,   MN 13 1300,   LG 28 5206,   EN   3 6801,   HE 51 6437
CS 24 6100,   SV 104 0500,   WA   0 1054,   SD   0 0153,   SW   0 0386

---- 897 VARIABLE L L   EMPLOYMENT BY SECTOR (MILLION PERSONS)

AG 341 7556,   MN 13 1297,   LG 28 5196,   EN   3 6802,   HE 51 6425
CS 24 6099,   SV 104 0472,   WA   0 1063,   SD   0 0153,   SW   0 0386

---- 897 PARAMETER K0   VOLUME OF CAPITAL STOCKS BY SECTOR
                          ('90 Y 100 MILLION)
AG 2480 0000,   MN 1546 2844,   LG 3288 7871,   EN 1465 4128
HE 7128 2787,   CS 1280 0000,   SV 13047 7193,   WA 53 6964
SD 15.3538,   SW 14 2857

---- 897 VARIABLE K L   CAPITAL STOCK BY SECTOR ('90 Y 100 MILLION)

AG 2479 9227,   MN 1546 3131,   LG 3288 6556,   EN 1465 4474
HE 7128 1939,   CS 1280 0083,   SV 13047 4973,   WA 54 1402
SD 15 3539,   SW 14 2858

---- 897 PARAMETER RUNEMP0   =   0 0400 UNEMPLOYMENT RATE (UNITLESS)
     VARIABLE RUNEMP L   =   0 0400 UNEMPLOYMENT RATE (UNITLESS)

---- 898 PARAMETER CD0   VOLUME OF HOUSEHOLD CONSUMPTION BY SECTOR
                          ('90 Y 100 MILLION)

AG 3058 9500,   MN 87 5200,   LG 2678 9200,   EN 100 3800
HE 937 5900,   SV 1869 0400

---- 898 VARIABLE CD L   FINAL DEMAND FOR PRIVATE CONSUMPTION
                           ('90 Y 100 MILLION)

AG 3058 8100,   MN 87 5160,   LG 2678 7876,   EN 100 3741
HE 937 5393,   SV 1868.9566

---- 898 PARAMETER TCD0   =   8732 4000 TOTAL HOUSEHOLD CONSUMPTION
                              IN THE BASE YEAR ('90 Y 100 MILLION)
     PARAMETER TCD   =   8731 9835 TOTAL HOUSEHOLD CONSUMPTION
                              ('90 Y 100 MILLION)

---- 898 PARAMETER GD0   VOLUME OF GOVERNMENT CONSUMPTION BY SECTOR
                          ('90 Y 100 MILLION)
AG 15 7500,   LG 173 3000,   HE 95 1600,   SV 1642 1400

---- 898 VARIABLE GD L   FINAL DEMAND FOR GOVERNMENT CONSUMPTION
                           ('90 Y 100 MILLION)
AG 15 7500,   LG 173 3000,   HE 95 1600,   SV 1642 1400

---- 898 PARAMETER INT0   VOLUME OF INTERMEDIATE INPUT DEMANDS
                           ('90 Y 100 MILLION)
AG 4133 2000,   MN 1353 2004,   LG 4161 9987,   EN 1367 9994
HE 10199 0001,   SV 3637 8011,   WA 18 3300,   SD   5 1800
SW   6 2900

138

---- 898 VARIABLE INT L   INTERMEDIATES USES ('90 Y 100 MILLION)

AG 4133 0513,   MN 1353 2004,   LG 4161 8762,   EN 1368 0421
HE 10198 8493,   SV 3637 7255,   WA 18 4815,   SD   5 1800
SW   6 2900

---- 898 PARAMETER ID0   VOLUME OF INVESTMENT BY SECTOR OF ORIGIN
                    ('90 Y 100 MILLION)
AG 131 0000,   LG 14 0000,   HE 1457 0000,   CS 3048 2100
SV 86 3540

---- 898 VARIABLE ID L   FINAL DEMAND FOR PRODUCTIVE INVESTMENT
                    ('90 Y 100 MILLION)
AG 131 0000,   LG 13 9997,   HE 1456 9992,   CS 3048 2063
SV 86 3540

---- 899 PARAMETER IDE0   VOLUME OF ENV INVESTMENT BY SECTOR OF
                    ORIGIN ('90 Y 100 MILLION)
LG 1 4700,   HE 32.6600

---- 899 VARIABLE IDE L   FINAL DEMAND FOR ENVIRONMENTAL INVESTMENT
                    ('90 Y 100 MILLION)
LG 1 4676,   HE 32 6621

---- 899 PARAMETER DST0   VOLUME OF INVENTORY INVESTMENT BY SECTOR
                    ('90 Y 100 MILLION)
AG 161 0500,   MN 6 1800,   LG 545 1600,   EN -59 4200,   HE 268 2100
SV 199 0300

---- 899 VARIABLE DST L   INVENTORY INVESTMENT BY SECTOR ('90 Y 100 MILLION)

AG 161 0434,   MN 6 1800,   LG 545 1393,   EN -59 4213,   HE 268 2055
SV 199 0256

---- 900 PARAMETER Y0   = 15928 6729 TOTAL VALUE-ADDED ('90 Y 100 MILLION)
        VARIABLE Y L   = 15928 2619 TOTAL VALUE-ADDED (CURR Y 100 MILLION)
        PARAMETER WL0   =   17 3066 AVERAGE WAGE RATE ('90 100 MILLION
                             YUAN PER MILLION WORKER)
        VARIABLE WL.L   =   17 3066 AVERAGE WAGE RATE (CURR Y 100 MILLION
                             PER MILLION PERSONS)
        PARAMETER WK0   =   0 2014 AVERAGE CAPITAL RETURN RATE (UNITLESS)
        VARIABLE WK L   =   0 2014 AVERAGE CAPITAL RETURN (UNITLESS)
        PARAMETER LBINC0 = 9822 6080 HOUSEHOLD LABOR INCOME
                             ('90 Y 100 MILLION)
        VARIABLE LBINC L = 9822 3203 PERSONAL INCOME (CURR Y 100 MILLION)
        PARAMETER YC0   = 6106 0649 ENTERPRISE CAPITAL INCOME
                             ('90 Y 100 MILLION)
        VARIABLE YC L   = 6105 9416 COMPANY REVENUE (CURR Y 100 MILLION)
        PARAMETER GR0   = 3701 1000 GOVERNMENT REVENUE ('90 Y 100 MILLION)
        VARIABLE GR L   = 3700 9760 GOVERNMENT REVENUE (CURR Y 100 MILLION)

---- 901 PARAMETER HHSAV0   = 1460 7900 HOUSEHOLD SAVING
                             ('90 Y 100 MILLION)
        VARIABLE HHSAV L   = 1460 7065 TOTAL HOUSEHOLD SAVING
                             (CURR Y 100 MILLION)
        PARAMETER CSAV0 = 2391 7300 SAVING BY COMPANY ('90 Y 100 MILLION)
        VARIABLE CSAV L = 2391 8397 TOTAL COMPANY SAVING
                             (CURR Y 100 MILLION)
        PARAMETER GSAV0 =   899 5500 GOVERNMENT SAVING ('90 Y 100 MILLION)
        VARIABLE GSAV L =   899 4265 GOVERNMENT SAVING (CURR Y 100 MILLION)

---- 902 PARAMETER SAVING0 = 6574 2200 TOTAL SAVING ('90 Y 100 MILLION)
        VARIABLE SAVING L = 6574 1373 TOTAL SAVING (CURR Y 100 MILLION)

VARIABLE INVEST L = 6574.1401 TOTAL INVESTMENT (CURR Y 100 MILLION)

---- 903 PARAMETER BSPLUS0 = 683.3200 SURPLUS IN BALANCE OF PAYMENT
('90 Y 100 MILLION)
VARIABLE BSPLUS.L = 683.2506 SURPLUS IN BALANCE OF PAYMENT
(CURR Y 100 MILLION)
PARAMETER DEFICIT0 = 139 6000 DEFICIT ('90 Y 100 MILLION)
VARIABLE DEFICIT L = 139.6000 GOVERNMENT BUDGET DEFICIT
(CURR Y 100 MILLION)

---- 904 PARAMETER GDPVA0 = 17113.6703 NOMINAL GDP IN THE BASE YEAR
('90 Y 100 MILLION)
VARIABLE GDPVA.L = 17113.1870 NOMINAL GDP IN MARKET PRICES
(CURR Y 100 MILLION)
PARAMETER RGDP0 = 17272.6540 REAL GDP IN THE BASE YEAR
('90 Y 100 MILLION)
VARIABLE RGDP.L = 17272.1415 REAL GDP ('90 Y 100 MILLION)

---- 905 PARAMETER PETAX0 POLLUTION EMISSION TAXES ('90 Y 100 MILLION)

	MN	LG	EN	HE
WA	0 1700	3.2000	0.3700	5.7800
SD	0.0800	0.6200	0.1400	1.4000
SW	0 0200	0.0700	0 0600	0.1600

---- 905 VARIABLE PETAX L POLLUTION EMISSION TAXES (CURR Y 100 MILLION)

	MN	LG	EN	HE
WA	0.1692	3.1841	0.3682	5.7513
SD	0.0800	0.6200	0.1400	1.4000
SW	0.0200	0.0700	0.0600	0.1600

---- 905 PARAMETER IMPL0 ADJUSTMENT FACTOR FOR POLLUTION EMISSION TAXES

	MN	LG	EN	HE
WA	0.0980	0.7640	0.2313	0.7795
SD	0.2239	1.0179	0.0784	1 3595
SW	0.0222	0.7005	0.3131	0.3660

---- 905 VARIABLE IMPL.L ADJUSTMENT PARAMETER FOR EMISSION TAX
IMPLEMENTATION (UNITLESS)

	MN	LG	EN	HE
WA	0.0980	0.7640	0.2313	0.7795
SD	0 2239	1.0179	0.0784	1.3595
SW	0.0222	0.7005	0.3131	0.3660

---- 906 PARAMETER PACOST0 POLLUTION ABATEMENT PAYMENTS ('90 Y 100 MILLION)

	MN	LG	EN	HE
WA	1.1400	3.4700	1 9500	11.7700
SD	0.2700	0.5700	2 4800	1.8600
SW	2.3200	0 3200	0 9200	2.7300

---- 906 VARIABLE PACOST.L POLLUTION ABATEMENT PAYMENTS
(CURR Y 100 MILLION)

	MN	LG	EN	HE
WA	1.1494	3.4986	1.9662	11.8673
SD	0.2700	0.5700	2.4801	1 8600
SW	2.3200	0.3200	0.9200	2.7300

---- 906 PARAMETER CL0 CLEANUP RATE BY POLLUTANT AND BY SECTOR (UNITLESS)

WA 0.3740, SD 0.7381, SW 0.9175

---- 906 VARIABLE CL.L   PERCENTAGE OF POLLUTANT ABATED (UNITLESS)

WA 0 3771, SD 0 7381, SW 0 9175

---- 907 PARAMETER PA0   PRICE OF POLLUTANT ABATED ('90 YUAN PER TON)

WA 0 4107, SD 86 5903, SW 1 0408

---- 907 VARIABLE PA L   PRICE(OR AVERAGE COST) OF POLLUTANT ABATED
                (CURR YUAN PER TON)
WA 0.4107, SD 86.5908, SW 1 0408

---- 908 PARAMETER DA0   POLLUTANT ABATED BY POLLUTANT AND BY
                SECTOR (100 MILLION TONS)
WA 44 6246, SD 0.0599, SW 6 0373

---- 908 VARIABLE DA L   POLLUTANT ABATED BY POLLUTANT AND BY
                SECTOR (100 MILLION TONS)
WA 44 9933, SD 0.0599, SW 6 0373

---- 908 PARAMETER TDA0   TOTAL POLLUTANT ABATED BY POLLUTANT
                (100 MILLION TONS)
WA 44 6246, SD 0.0599, SW 6 0373

---- 908 VARIABLE TDA L   TOTAL POLLUTANT ABATED BY POLLUTANT (100
                MILLION TONS)
WA 44 9933, SD 0 0599, SW 6 0373

---- 908 PARAMETER DG0   TOTAL AMOUNT OF POLLUTION GENERATION BY
                POLLUTANT (100 MILLION TONS)
WA 282.2703, SD 0 0907, SW 7 1534

---- 908 VARIABLE DG.L   TOTAL AMOUNT OF POLLUTION GENERATION BY
                POLLUTANT (100 MILLION TONS)
WA 282 2643, SD 0.0907, SW 7.1533

---- 908 PARAMETER DE0   TOTAL AMOUNT OF POLLUTION DISCHARGED (100
                MILLION TONS)
WA 237 6457, SD 0.0308, SW 1 1161

---- 908 VARIABLE DE L   TOTAL AMOUNT OF POLLUTION DISCHARGED (100
                MILLION TONS)
WA 237 2710, SD 0.0308, SW 1 1160

---- 909 PARAMETER ETAX0 = 12 0700 TOTAL POLLUTION EMISSION TAX REVENUE
                ('90 Y 100 MILLION)
      VARIABLE ETAX L = 12.0226 TOTAL POLLUTION EMISSION TAX REVENUE
                (CURR Y 100 MILLION)
      PARAMETER DTAX0 = 0 0000 TOTAL HOUSEHOLD WASTE DISPOSAL TAX
                ('90 Y 100 MILLION)
      VARIABLE DTAX.L = 0.0000 TOTAL HOUSEHOLD POLLUTION DISPOSAL
                TAX (CURR Y 100 MILLION)

---- 910 PARAMETER DSUB0 = 0 0000   GOVERNMENT SUBSIDY TO POLLUTION
                CONTROL ('90 Y 100 MILLION)
      VARIABLE DSUB.L = 0.0000 GOVERNMENT SUBSIDY TO POLLUTION CONTROL
                (CURR Y 100 MILLION)
      PARAMETER DCOMPEN0 = 0 3874 TOTAL ENVIRONMENTAL COMPENSATION
                ('90 Y 100 MILLION)
      VARIABLE DCOMPEN.L = 0 3865 TOTAL COMPENSATION FOR POLLUTION DAMAGE
                (CURR Y 100 MILLION)

141

---- 911 PARAMETER UTILITY0   =   9 3226 INITIAL VALUE OF UTILITY
                                    ('90 Y 100 MILLION)
    VARIABLE UTILITY L = 9 3267 THE VALUE OF SOCIAL WELFARE FUNCTION
    VARIABLE OMEGA L = 7.291998E-5 OBJECTIVE FUNCTION VARIABLE
                                    ('90 Y 100 MILLION)

---- 912 VARIABLE WAL L   SLACK VARIABLES

MN 5 239775E-6,   LG 3 247903E-7,   EN 2 129858E-6,   CS 2 259252E-7
SV -1 15139E-7,   WA   -0 0016,   SD   0 0053,   SW   -0 0065

EXECUTION TIME   =   0 600 SECONDS   VERID MW2-00-064

**** FILE SUMMARY

INPUT   C:\GAMS386\A GMS
OUTPUT   C:\GAMS386\A LST

Bibliography

Adelman, I. and Robinson, S. (1978), *Income Distribution Policy in Developing Countries: A Case Study of Korea*, Standford University Press.

Ahmad, Y. J., El Serafy, S. and Lutz, E. (1989*), Environmental Accounting for Sustainable Development*, A UNEP-World Bank Symposium, the World Bank.

Armington, P. (1969), 'A Theory of Demand for Products Distinguished by Place of Production', *IMF Staff Papers*, Vol.16, 159-76.

Arrow, K. (1974), 'General Economic Equilibrium: Purpose, Analytic Techniques, Collective Choice', *The American Economic Review*, Vol.64, No.3, 253-72.

Azis, I. (1993), 'Computable General Equilibrium Model for Linking Pollution and Macroeconomic Variables', Cornell University City and Regional Planning Working Paper, No.136, Ithaca, NY.

Azis, I. (1994), 'Impacts of SSA-Program on Rural-Urban Welfare: A General Equilibrium Framework', Cornell University City and Regional Planning Working Paper, No.127, Ithaca, NY.

Ballard, C.L., Fullerton, D., Shoven, J.B. and Whalley, J. (1985), *A General Equilibrium Model for Tax Policy Evaluation*, The University of Chicago Press: Chicago.

Ballard, C.L. and Medema, S.G. (1993), 'The Marginal Efficiency Effects of Taxes and Subsidies in the Presence of Externalities: A Computable General Equilibrium Approach', *Journal of Public Economics*, No.52, 199-216.

Bartelmus, P., Stahmer, C. and van Tongeren, J. (1993), 'Integrated Environmental and Economic Accounting - A Framework for an SNA Satellite System', in Lutz, E. (ed.) *Toward Improved Accounting for the Environment*, The World Bank, Washington, D.C.

Beghin, J., Roland-Holst, D. and van der Mensbrugghe, D. (1994), 'Trade Liberalization and the Environment in the Pacific Basin: Coordinated Approaches to Mexican Trade and Environmental Policy', presented at the 1995 ASSA meeting, Washington, D.C., January 7-9, 1995, mimeo, processed.

Bergman, L. (1985), 'Extensions and Applications of the MSG-Model: A Brief Survey', in Forsund, F.R., Hoel, M. and Longva, S. (eds.) *Production, Multi-sectoral Growth and Planning: Essays in Memory of Leif Johansen*, North-Holland Publishing House: Amsterdam.

Bergman, L. (1988), 'Energy Policy Modeling: A Survey of General Equilibrium Approaches', *Journal of Policy Modeling*, Vol.10, No.3, 377-99.

Bergman, L., Jorgenson, D.W. and Zalai, E. (1990a), *General Equilibrium Modeling and Economic Policy Analysis*, Basil Blackwell: Oxford.

Bergman, L. (1990b), 'Energy and Environmental Constraints on Growth: A CGE-Modeling Approach', *Journal of Policy Modeling*, Vol.12, No.4, 671-91.

Bergman, L. (1991), 'General Equilibrium Effects of Environmental Policy: A CGE-Modeling Approach', *Environmental and Resource Economics*, Vol.1, No.1, 43-61.

Bergman, L. (1993), 'General Equilibrium Costs and Benefits of Environmental Policies: Some Preliminary Results Based on Swedish Data', mimeo, processed.

Blitzer, C., et al. (1992), 'Growth and Welfare Losses from Carbon Emissions Restrictions: A General Equilibrium Analysis for Egypt', Working Paper, Center for Energy Policy Research, MIT, Cambridge, MA.

Boyd, R. and Uri, N.D. (1991), 'The Cost of Improving the Quality of the Environment', *Environment and Planning A*, Vol.23, 1163-82.

Byrd, W. A. (1987), 'The Impact of the Two-Tier Plan/Market System in Chinese Industry', *Journal of Comparative Economics*, Vol.11, 295-308.

Byrd, W. A. (1989), 'Plan and Market in the Chinese Economy: A Simple General Equilibrium Model', *Journal of Comparative Economics*, Vol.13, 177-204.

Chen, B. (1994), *Ke Ji Suan Yi Ban Jun Heng Mo Xin: Li Lueng, Suan Fa Yu Yin Yong (Computable General Equilibrium Model: Theory, Algorithm and Application)*, unpublished Ph.D. dissertation, Chinese Academy of Sciences, Beijing.

Chenery, H., Robinson, S. and Syrquin, M. (1986), *Industrialization and Growth: A Comparative Study*, Published for the World Bank. Oxford University Press: Oxford.

Chiang, A.C. (1967), *Fundamental Methods of Mathematic Economics*, 2nd Edition, McGraw-Hill: New York.

Condon, T., Dahl, H. and Devarajan, S. (1986), Implementing A Computable General Equilibrium Model on GAMS: The Cameroon Model, *DRD Discussion Paper*, Report No. DRD290, The World Bank, Washington.

Conrad, K. and Schroder, M. (1993), 'Choosing Environmental Policy Instruments Using General Equilibrium Models', *Journal of Policy Modeling*, Vol.15, No.5&6, 521-43.

Copeland, B.R. and Taylor, M.S. (1994), 'North-South Trade and the Environment', *The Quarterly Journal of Economics*, August 1994.

de Haan, M., Keuning, S. and Bosch, P. (1993), 'Integrated Indicators in a National Accounting Matrix Including Environmental Accounts (NAMEA)', *National Accounts Occasional Paper*, No.NA-060, Netherlands Central Bureau of Statistics.

Decaluwe, B. and Martens, A. (1987), 'Developing Countries and General Equilibrium Models: A Review of the Empirical Literature', *IDRC Report*, No. IDRC-MR155e, International Development Research Center, Ottawa, Canada.

Defourny, J. and Thorbecke, E. (1984), 'Structural Path Analysis and Multiplier Decomposition with a Social Accounting Matrix Framework', *The Economic Journal*, Vol.94, March, 111-36.

den Hartog, H., and Houweling, A. (1976), 'Pollution, Pollution Abatement, and the Economic Structure of the Netherlands', in Polenske, K.R. and Skolka, J.V. (ed.), *Advances in Input-Output Analysis*, proceedings of the Sixth International Conference on Input-Output Techniques, Vienna, April 22-26, 1974, Ballinger: Cambridge, MA.

Dervis, K., de Melo, J. and Robinson, S. (1982), *General Equilibrium Models for Development Policy*, Cambridge University Press: London.

Devarajan, S., Lewis, J.D. and Robinson, S. (1986), 'A Bibliography of Computable General Equilibrium (CGE) Models Applied to Developing Countrie', Working Paper No.400, *Dept. of Agricultural and Resource Economics*, University of California, Berkeley.

Devarajan, S. (1988), 'Lecture Notes on Computable General Equilibrium Models', John F. Kennedy School of Government, Harvard University, mimeo, processed.

Devarajan, S., Lewis, J.D. and Robinson, S. (1990), 'Policy Lessons from Trade-Focused, Two-Secotr Models', *Journal of Policy Modeling*, Vol.12, No.4, 625-57.

Devarajan, S., Lewis, J.D. and Robinson, S. (1991), *From Stylied to Applied Models: Building Multisector CGE Models for Policy Analysis*, mimeo, processed.

Devarajan, S. (1993a), 'Can Computable General-Equilibrium Models Shed Light on the Environmental Problems of Developing Countries?' mimeo, processed.

Devarajan, S. and Go, D. (1993b), 'The Simplest Dynamic General Equilibrium Model of an Open Economy', mimeo, processed

Devarajan, S., Lewis, J.D. and Robinson, S. (forthcoming), *Getting the Model Right: the General Equilibrium Approach to Adjustment Policy*, Cambridge University Press: London.

Dinwiddy, C.L. and Teal, F.J. (1988), *The Two-Sector General Equilibrium Model: A New Approach*, Philip Allan/St. Martin's Press: New York.

Dowlatabadi, H., Goulder, L. H. and Kopp, R. (1994). 'Integrated Economic and Ecological Modeling for Public Policy Decision Making', *Resources for the Future Working Papers*, Washington.

Dufournaud, M.C., Harrington, J. and Rogers, P. (1988), 'Leontief's "Environmental Repercussions and the Economic Structure..." Revisited: A General Equilibrium Formulation', *Geographical Analysis*, Vol.20, No.4, 318-27.

Espinosa, J.A. and Smith, V.K. (1994), 'Measuring the Environmental Consequences of Trade Policy: A Non-Market CGE Analysis', Paper prepared for the 1995 ASSA meeting, Washington, D.C. January 7-9, 1995.

Fargeix, A. and Sadoulet, E. (1994), 'A Financial Computable General Equilibrium Model for the Analysis of Stabilization Programs', in Mercenier, J. and Srinivasan, T.N. (ed.), *Applied General Equilibrium and Economic Development: Present Achievements and Future Trends*, The University of Michigan Press: Ann Arbor.

Florig, K., et al. (1995), 'China Strives to Make the Polluter Pay: Are China's Market-based Incentives for Improved Environmental Compliance Working?' *Environmental Science & Technology*, Vol.29, No.6, 268-73.

Forsund, F.R. and Storm, S. (1988), *Environmental Economics and Management: Pollution and Natural Resources*, Croom Helm: London.

146

Forsund, F.R., Hoel, M. and Longva, S. (1985), *Production, Multi-sectoral Growth and Planning: Essays in Memory of Leif Johansen*, North-Holland Publishing Company: Amsterdam.

Fox, H.L. and Schachter, G. (1975), 'Dynamics of Structural Change', *Regional Science and Urban Economics*, Vol.5, 41-57.

Garbaccio, R. (1994), *Reform and Structural Change in the Chinese Economy: A CGE Analysis*, unpublished Ph.D. Dissertation, University of California, Berkeley.

Glomsrod, S., Vennemo, H. and Johnson, T. (1992), 'Stabilization of Emissions of CO_2: A Computable General Equilibrium Assessment', *Scandinavian Journal of Economics*, Vol.94, No.1, 53-69.

Hazilla, M. and Kopp, R. (1990), 'Social Cost of Environmental Quality Regulations: A General Equilibrium Analysis', *Journal of Political Economy*, Vol.98, No.4, 853-73.

Hordijk, L. (1983), 'Economic Structural and the Environment: Production, Pollution and Energy Comsumption in the Netherlands, 1973/1985', in Lakshmanan, T.R. and Nijkamp, P. (ed.), *Systems and Models for Energy and Environmental Analysis*, Gower: Aldershot, Hamphire.

Hudson, E.A. and Jorgenson, D.W. (1974), 'U.S. Energy Policy and Economic Growth, 1975-2000'. *Bell Journal of Economics and Management Sciences*, August, 461-514.

Idenburg, A. and Steenge, A. (1991), 'Environmental Policy in Single-product and Joint Production Input-Output Models', in Dietz, F.J. et al. (eds.), *Environmental Policy and the Economy*, North-Holland Publishing Company: Amsterdam.

Isard, W., et al. (1971), *Ecological-Economic Analysis for Regional Planning*, The Free Press: New York.

Johansen, L. (1974), *A Multi-sectoral Study of Economic Growth*, Second, enlarged edition, North-Holland Publishing Company: Amsterdam.

Johnson, M.H. and Bennett, J.T. (1981), 'Regional Environmental and Economic Impact Evaluation: An Input-Output Approach', *Regional Science and Urban Economics*, Vol.11, 215-30.

Jones, R. (1965), 'The Structure of Simple General Equilibrium Models', *The Journal of Political Economy*, Vol.123, No.6, 557-72.

Jorgenson, D.W. (1984), 'Econometric Methods for Applied General Equilibrium Analysis', in Scarf, H.E. and Shoven, J.B. (eds), *Applied General Equilibrium Analysis*, Cambridge University Press: London.

Jorgenson, D.W. and Slesnick, D.T. (1985), 'Efficiency versus Equity in Natural Gas Price Regulation', *Journal of Econometrics*, Vol.30, October/November, 302-16.

Jorgenson, D.W. and Wilcoxen, P.J. (1990), 'Intertemporal General Equilibrium Modeling of U.S. Environmental Regulation', *Journal of Policy Modeling*, Vol.12, No.4, 715-44.

Jorgenson, D.W. and Wilcoxen, P.J. (1993), 'Reducing U.S. Carbon Dioxide Emissions: An Assessment of Different Instruments', *Journal of Policy Modeling*, Vol.15, No.5&6, 491-520.

Keuning, S. (1993), 'National Accounts and the Environment: the Case for a System's Approach', *National Accounts Occasional Paper*, No.NA-053, Netherlands Central Bureau of Statistics.

Keuning, S. (1994), 'The SAM and Beyond: Open, SESAME!' *Economic Systems Research*, Vol.6, No.1, 21-50.

Kim, E. (1991), *Regional Equity and Economic Development Policy: An Interregional CGE Model for Korea*, unpublished PhD Dissertation. Cornell University, Ithaca, NY.

King, B.B. (1985), 'What is a SAM?' in Pyatt G. and Round, J.I. (eds.), *Social Accounting Matrices: A Basis for Planning*, A World Bank Symposium, The World Bank, Washington, D.C.

Kohn, R. (1975). 'Input-Output Analysis and Air Pollution Control', in Mills, E. (ed.), *Economic Analysis of Environmental Problems*, National Bureau of Economic Research, New York.

Kokoski, M.F. and Smith, V.K. (1987), 'A General Equilibrium Analysis of Partial-Equilibrium Welfare Measures: The Case of Climate Change', *The American Economic Review*, Vol.77, No.3, 331-41.

Lee, H. and Roland-Holst, D. (1993), 'International Trade and the Transfer of Environmental Costs and Benefits', *OECD Development Centre Technical Papers*, No.91, OECD, Paris.

Leontief, W. (1970), 'Environmental Repercussions and the Economic Structure: An Input-Output Approach', *Review of Economics and Statistics*, Vol.52, No.3, 262-71.

Leontief, W. and Ford, D. (1972), 'Air Pollution and Economic Structure: Empirical Results of Input-Output Computations', in Brody, A. and Carter, A.P. (eds.), *Input-Output Techniques*, Proceedings of the Fifth International Conference on Input-Output Techniques, Geneva, 1971, American Elsevier: New York.

Lewis, J. (1993), 'Energy Pricing, Economic Distortion, and Air Pollution in Indonesia', *HIID Development Discussion Paper*, No.455, Harvard Institute for International Development, Harvard University: Cambridge.

Lluch, C., Powell, A. and Williams, R. (1977), *Patterns in Household Demand and Saving*, Oxford University Press: Oxford.

Lutz, E. (1993), *Toward Improved Accounting for the Environment*, An UNSTAT-World Bank Symposium, The World Bank, Washington, D.C.

Mansur, A. and Whalley, J. (1994), 'Numerical Specification of Applied General Equilibrium Models: Estimation, Calibration, and Data' in Scarf H.E. and Shoven, J.B. (eds.), *Applied General Equilibrium Analysis*, Cambridge University Press: London.

Martin, W. (1993), 'Modeling the Post-Reform Chinese Economy', *Journal of Policy Modeling*, Vol.15, No.5&6, 545-79.

McKibbin, W.J. and Wilcoxen, P.J. (1995), 'Environmental Policy and International Trade', *Brookings Discussion Paper in International Economics*, No.117, The Brookings Institution, Washington, D.C.

McKibbin, W.J. and Wilcoxen, P.J. (1995), 'The Theoretical and Empirical Structure of the G-Cubed Model', *Brookings Discussion Paper in International Economics*, No.118, The Brookings Institution, Washington, D.C.

Meeraus, A. (1983), 'An Algebraic Approach to Modeling', *Journal of Economic Dynamics and Control*, Vol.5, 81-108.

Miller, R.E. and Blair, P.D. (1985), *Input-Output Analysis: Foundations and Extensions*, Prentice-Hall, Inc: New Jersey.

National Environmental Protection Agency of China (NEPA), (1991a), *China Environmental Yearbook* (series), China Environmental Science Publishing House: Beijing.

National Environmental Protection Agency of China (NEPA), (1991b), *1990 Environmental Annual Report* (internal report), National Environmental Protection Agency of China, Beijing.

National Environmental Protection Agency of China (NEPA), (1992), Pollution Charge in China, National Environmental Protection Agency of China, Beijing.

Nestor, D.V. and Pasurka, C.A. (1995), 'CGE Model of Pollution Abatement Processes for Assessing the Economic Effects of Environmental Policy', *Economic Modelling*, Vol.12, No.1, 53-9.

Pearce, D.W. and Turner, R.K. (1990), *Economics of Natural Resources and the Environment*, The Johns Hopkins University Press: Baltimore.

Persson, A.B. (1994), 'Deforestation in Costa Rica: Investigating the Impacts of Market Failures and Unwanted Side Effects of Macro Policies Using Three Different Modeling Approaches', *Beijer Discussion Series Paper*, No.48, Beijer Institute for International Ecological Economics, Swedish Royal Academy of Sciences, Stockholm.

Peskin, H.M. and Lutz, E. (1993), 'A Survey of Resource and Environmental Accounting Approaches in Industrialized Countries', in E. Lutz (ed.), *Toward Improved Accounting for the Environment*, An UNSTAT-World Bank Symposium, The World Bank, Washington, D.C.

Piggott, J., Whalley, J. and Wigle, R. (1992), 'International Linkages and Carbon Reduction Initiatives', in Anderson, K. and Blackhurst, R. (eds.), *The Greening of World Trade Issues*, The University of Michigan Press: Ann Arbor.

Piggott, J., Whalley, J. and Wigle, R. (1993), 'How Large Are the Incentives to Join Subglobal Carbon-Reduction Initiatives?' *Journal of Policy Modeling*, Vol.15, No.5&6, 473-90.

Pyatt, G. and Roe, A.S. (1978), *Social Accounting for Development Planning: with Special Reference to Sri Lanka*, Cambridge University Press: London.

Pyatt, G. (1988), 'A SAM Approach to Modeling', *Journal of Policy Modeling*, Vol.10, No.3, 327-352.

Robinson, S. and Roland-Holst, D.W. (1988), 'Macroeconomic Structure and Computable General Equilibrium Models', *Journal of Policy Modeling*. Vol.10, No.3, 353-57.

Robinson, S. (1989), 'Multisectoral Models', in Chenery, H. and Srinivasan, T.H. (eds.), *Handbook of Development Economics*, Elsevier Science Publishers: New York.

Robinson, S. (1990), 'Pollution, Market Failure, and Optimal Policy in an Economy-wide Framework', *Agricultural and Resource Economics Working Paper*, No.559, University of California, Berkeley.

Robinson, S. (1991), 'Macroeconomics, Financial Variables, and Computable General Equilibrium Models', *World Development*, Vol.19, No.11, 1509-25.

Robinson, S., Subramanian, S. and Geoghegan, J. (1993), 'Modeling Air Pollution Abatement in a Market Based Incentive Framework for the Los Angeles Basin', mimeo, processed.

Rose, A. (1974), 'A Dynamic Interindustry Model for the Economic Analysis of Pollution Abatement', *Environment and Planning A*, Vol.8, 321-338.

Ruth, M. (1993), *Integrating Economics, Ecology and Thermodynamics*, Kluwer Academic Publishers: Boston.

Rutherford, T.F. (1994), 'Applied General Equilibrium Modeling with MPSGE as a GAME Subsystem', mimeo, processed.

Scarf, H.E. (1967), 'The Computation of Equilibrium Prices', reprinted in Scarf, H.E. and Shoven, J.B. (eds. 1984), *Applied General Equilibrium Analysis*, Cambridge University Press: London.

Scarf, H.E. and Shoven, J.B. (1984), *Applied General Equilibrium Analysis*, Cambridge University Press: London.

Shoven, J.B. and Whalley, J. (1984), 'Applied General-Equilibrium Models of Taxation and International Trade: An Introduction and Survey', *Journal of Economic Literature*, Vol.22, 1007-51.

State Statistical Bureau of China (SSB), (1991), *China Statistical Yearbook* (series), China Statistical Publishing House: Beijing.

State Statistical Bureau of China (SSB), (1993), *1990 Input-Output Table of China*, China Statistical Publishing House: Beijing.

Stone, R. (1962), 'Multiple Classification in Social Accounting', *Bulletin of the International Statistical Institute*, Vol.3, 215-233.

Syrquin, M. (1989). 'Patterns of Structural Change', in Chenery, H. and Srinivasan, T.N. (eds.), *Handbook of Development Economics*, Elsevier Science Publishers: New York.

Taylor, L. (1990), 'Structuralist CGE Models', in Taylor, L. (ed.), *Socially Relevant Policy Analysis: Structuralist Computable General Equilibrium Models for the Developing World*, The MIT Press: Cambridge, MA.

Thorbecke, E. (1992), *Adjustment and Equity in Indonesia*, OECD, Paris.

United Nations, (1993a), *Revised System of National Accounts, Studies in Methods*, Series F, 2, Rev.4, United Nations, New York.

United Nations, (1993b), *Integrated Environmental and Economic Accounting* (Interim version), Studies in Methods, Series F, 61, United Nations: New York.

Wang, Z. (1994), *The Impact of Economic Integration among Taiwan, Hong Kong and China*, unpublished Ph.D. Dissertation, University of Minnesota.

World Bank, (1985a), *China: Long-Term Development Issues and Options*, The Johns Hopkins University Press: Baltimore.

World Bank, (1985b), *China Economic Model and Projections, Annex 4 to China: Long-Term Development Issues and Options*, The World Bank: Washington, D.C.

World Bank, (1990), *China: Between Plan and Market*, The World Bank: Washington, D.C.

World Bank, (1992), *China: Reform and the Role of the Plan in the 1990s*, The World Bank: Washington, D.C.

World Bank, (1993), *China: The Achievement and Challenge of Price Reform*, The World Bank: Washington, D.C.

World Bank, (1994a), *China: Internal Market Development and Regulation*, The World Bank: Washington, D.C.

World Bank, (1994b), *China: Foreign Trade Reform*, The World Bank, Washington: D.C.

Xie, J. (1993), *Humanity and Nature: An Environmental History of Contemporary China*, mimeo.

Xu, D. (1993), 'Price Distortion in the Transition Process: A CGE Analysis of China's Case', *Economics of Planning*, Vol.26, 161-82.

Zhang, K., et al. (1992), *China Environmental Protection Investment Report*, Tsinghua University Press: Beijing.